Glencoe

WORLD HISTORY

Standardized Test Skills
Practice Workbook

TEACHER ANNOTATED EDITION

Glencoe
McGraw-Hill

New York, New York   Columbus, Ohio   Chicago, Illinois   Peoria, Illinois   Woodland Hills, California

Text
5 From the *Iliad* by Homer translated by E.V. Rieu, copyright © 1966 by E.V. Rieu.
23 From "Life of Leonardo da Vinci" in *Lives of the Most Eminent Painters, Sculptors, and Architects* by Giorgio Vasari, translated by Gaston De C De Vere, copyright © 1912
48 From *Grapes of Wrath* by John Steinbeck copyright © 1939 by John Steinbeck
52 Speech by Adolf Hitler, from *The Rise and Fall of the Third Reich* by William Shrier
54 Editorial from the *Dallas Morning News,* March 2, 1998
59 From "Emotional Visit to Robben Island for Clinton and Mandela," Africa News Online, copyright © 1998 PanAfrican News Agency. Distributed via **Africa News Online (www.africanews.org)**

Photographs
14 Metropolitan Museum of Art, New York
22 SuperStock
24 (L) Biblioteca Nazionale, Turin/Bridgeman Art Library, London/New York
(R) Biblioteca Ambrosiana, Milan/Bridgeman Art Library, London/New York
27 SuperStock
29 SuperStock
40 File Photo
47 Library of Congress
50 The Museum of Modern Art, New York. Given anonymously. Photograph 1998 The Museum of Modern Art, New York
51 National Archives Still Picture Branch
57 SuperStock

Glencoe/McGraw-Hill
A Division of The **McGraw·Hill** Companies

Send all inquiries:
Glencoe/McGraw-Hill
8787 Orion Place
Columbus, Ohio 43240-4027

ISBN 0-07-829447-9

Printed in the United States of America

1 2 3 4 5 6 7 8 9 10   009   08 07 06 05 04 03 02

TABLE OF CONTENTS

Objectives Addressed in the Activities

The objectives in this workbook are addressed in many standardized social studies tests. The activities in the workbook give students the opportunity to practice the skills related to these objectives.

The student will:

- identify supporting ideas in a variety of written texts.
- analyze information in a variety of written texts in order to make inferences and generalizations.
- summarize a variety of written texts.
- respond appropriately in a written composition to the purpose/audience specified in a given topic.
- interpret maps to answer geographic questions, infer geographic relationships, and analyze geographic change.
- perceive relationships and recognize outcomes in a variety of written texts.
- recognize points of view, propaganda, and/or statements of fact and nonfact in a variety of written texts.
- organize ideas in a written composition on a given topic.
- analyze information and form hypotheses.
- express or solve problems using mathematical representation.
- generate a written composition that develops/supports/elaborates the central idea stated in a given topic.
- evaluate the reasonableness of a solution to a problem situation.

Workbook Overview

This workbook helps you prepare for standardized tests. Standardized tests in social studies cover many types of skills, some of which overlap with the skills found in other subject areas, such as mathematics, reading, and writing.

These activities provide practice with the following social studies skills:

- analyzing statistics
- detecting bias and analyzing propaganda
- forming hypotheses and predicting outcomes
- interpreting and constructing graphs and graphic organizers
- interpreting political cartoons
- making decisions and solving problems
- making inferences and drawing conclusions
- outlining information
- reading and writing about social studies topics
- reading maps
- taking notes
- thinking critically
- understanding historical and geographical concepts
- understanding the main idea of a passage
- using primary and secondary sources
- writing a unified essay

In addition, the activities in this workbook provide practice in three major question formats:

- multiple choice
- open-ended short response
- open-ended extended response

PREPARING FOR A STANDARDIZED TEST

Learning About the Test

Standardized tests differ from one another. Students need to familiarize themselves with the specific test they must take. How can they best do this? There are three steps in preparing for any test. Students should:

- read about the test.
- review the content covered by the test.
- practice on questions like those on the test.

Reading About the Test

Inform students of the sources they can consult to learn about the test. Students should:

- know that they can always prepare for a test. At the very least, students can familiarize themselves with the format of the test, the types of questions that will be asked, and the amount of time they will have to complete the test.
- use materials from The Princeton Review and Glencoe/McGraw-Hill to learn about their particular test.
- read any information the state or testing company releases. Sometimes the test-writers will release information through the school. If they do not, students can look for information on the Internet site of the testing company or state board of education.

Reviewing the Content Covered by the Test

In addition to learning about the format of the test, students will benefit from reviewing the subject matter covered on the test. This will ensure that they are ready for both what the test asks and how it does so.

If there are specific objectives or standards that are tested on the exam your students must take, help them review the facts or skills specified by each standard in advance to be sure they are proficient in them. This workbook can help you do this. Each activity focuses on a common social studies objective. You can assign the activities in order, or focus on those that are most important for the test your students will take.

Practicing

The most important part of a student's preparation for any standardized test is extensive practice. Practice tests allow students to become familiar with the content, format, and timing of the real exam. Reviewing the practice tests also allows students to review specific areas covered by the exam, to understand why they chose wrong answers, and to learn to avoid choosing wrong answers in the future. Students should:

- practice all the types of questions they will encounter on their test—multiple choice, short response, and extended response. Students should practice on real released tests whenever possible.
- understand the guidelines that will be used to evaluate their constructed responses. Students cannot meet the guidelines utilized by the test scorers if they are unfamiliar with the guidelines.

Helping Students Apply What They Know About the Test

Make sure students know that they should pace themselves, use the order of difficulty when it is applicable, guess when it is beneficial, and use the process of elimination to score their highest.

Pacing

Students should pace themselves differently depending on how the test is administered.

- If the test is timed, students should work carefully but not allow themselves to become stuck on any one question. As they practice, they should try to increase the number of questions they can complete correctly within the time limit.
- If the test is untimed, students should work slowly and carefully. If they have trouble with an item, they should mark it and come back to it later. Students should keep in mind that they have no time limit, so they should not let themselves speed up unnecessarily.

Using the Order of Difficulty

Not all standardized tests are arranged in order of question difficulty, but some are.

- If the test questions are arranged in order of difficulty, then the questions run from easy to medium to difficult, in that order. Students should be certain that they correctly complete the easy and medium questions before moving on to the most difficult questions.
- As they enter the difficult sections of a test that progresses from easy to difficult, students should be aware that answer choices may be misleading. The obvious answer is probably not the correct answer to a difficult question.
- If the questions are not arranged in order of difficulty (that is, any question at any point could be easy, medium, or difficult), students should skip through the test, answering all the easier questions. Then they can go back and answer the more difficult items.

Guessing

Some tests impose a penalty for incorrect answers, usually a fraction of a point. Others do not. Find out if the test your students must take imposes a guessing penalty.

- If there is no penalty for incorrect answers, then students should answer every single question, even if they do not have time to read it.
- If there is a penalty for incorrect answers, then students should only answer a question if they have read it, understood it, and are able to eliminate at least one answer choice.

Using the Process of Elimination

For any multiple choice question, students should know how to quickly and effectively use the process of elimination to narrow down the possible answer choices. Even when they are certain they know which answer is best, students should always confirm their knowledge by reading the other choices and eliminating them.

What is the capital of Western Samoa?
A   Peru
B   London
C   Vila
D   Apia

The question above might be difficult for many students to answer. However, most students will easily be able to eliminate choices A and B, leaving them with a 50 percent chance of guessing correctly. If students do not eliminate any answer choices, they have only a 25 percent chance of guessing correctly.

Students should physically cross out answer choices they have eliminated (whenever the testing situation allows) so that they do not mistakenly fill in an answer oval for a choice they have mentally eliminated. Crossing out eliminated choices also ensures that students will not waste time rereading an answer that they know is wrong.

If a test has a definite order of difficulty, students should be aware that toward the end of the test it will be harder to eliminate choices, since the answer choices may involve vocabulary and/or concepts with which students are unfamiliar. Students should be sure to eliminate only those choices they understand completely and are certain are incorrect.

Right Before the Test

Students should be sure to do the following:

- Get at least eight hours of sleep each night for the week leading up to the test.
- Eat a nutritious breakfast.
- Bring any necessary paperwork with them to the test, such as identification and registration forms.
- Have plenty of sharpened pencils and erasers available.
- Complete a few easy warm-up questions the morning of the test, allowing themselves to get into test-taking gear.

Standardized Test Skills Practice

ACTIVITY 1
Arranging Events in Sequential Order

Social Studies Objective: The student will identify supporting ideas in a variety of written texts.

*I*n order to understand what you are reading, you must be able to arrange events in **sequential order.** This means organizing the events into a logical, orderly pattern based on when they happened. Creating a **time line** is one of the best ways to arrange events sequentially. A time line is a graphic illustration that shows events in order of occurrence over a particular period of time. It is easier to understand the order of events and their relationship to one another if the events are seen in chronological sequence on a time line.

★ Learning to Arrange Events in Sequential Order

Use the following steps to understand how events are arranged in sequential order on a time line:

- Read the time line's title to determine its purpose.
- Look at the span of years and the number of events.

- Identify the relationships among the events.
- Draw conclusions or inferences from your study.

★ Practicing the Skill

DIRECTIONS: Study the example of a time line below and complete the activity that follows.

Prehistoric Times

c. 3,000,000 B.C. Early humans make the first stone tools

c. 1,400,000 B.C. Early humans discover fire

c. 100,000 B.C. Neanderthals spread from Africa into Europe and Asia

c. 50,000 B.C. Early humans acquire language

c. 10,000 B.C. Neolithic Age begins

c. 8000 B.C. Agriculture begins in various places

c. 5500 B.C. Humans invent writing

Name _____ Date _____ Class _____

_____

DIRECTIONS: A time line provides an organized look at a sequence of events. In the space provided below, create your own time line that shows the major events of your own life from birth to the present.

Title: _____

Student answers will vary.

To complete the time line, students should select key dates in their lives, such as their dates of birth, first day of school, school graduations, and so on.

 Standardized Test Skills Practice

DIRECTIONS: Using the time line on the previous page, answer the following questions.

1 Which event occurred first?

   A beginning of Neolithic Age

   B rise of agriculture

  ***C** discovery of fire

   D acquiring of language

2 Which entry on the time line comes before "Early humans discover fire"?

   F "Humans invent writing"

   G "Neolithic Age begins"

  ***H** "Early humans make the first stone tools"

   J "Early humans acquire language"

Standardized Test Skills Practice

ACTIVITY 2
Interpreting Charts and Tables

Social Studies Objective: The student will analyze information in a variety of written texts in order to make inferences and generalizations.

So that relationships can be seen, a **chart** or **table** is often used to organize data. A table, for example, may show population trends over a period of time. After studying the data in a table, you will be able to analyze trends or patterns. Information in a chart may compare several elements of several items. Charts are good for organizing and comparing data.

★ Learning to Interpret Charts and Tables

Use the following guidelines to help you interpret data in tables and charts.

- Read the chart's title to determine its subject.
- Read each column's heading and each row's label.
- Study the data vertically in each column and horizontally across the rows.
- Identify relationships and contrasts and draw conclusions.

★ Practicing the Skill

DIRECTIONS: Use the information in the chart below to complete the activity that follows.

Selected Peoples of Ancient Southwest Asia			
Characteristics	Phoenicians c. 1100 B.C.	Israelites c. 1000 B.C.	Persians c. 500 B.C.
Expansion	Established colonies around the Mediterranean Sea	Exiled in Babylon	Conquered the area from the Nile River to the Indus River
Contributions	Used alphabet of 22 characters for record keeping	Stressed the concept of the worth of the individual	Built cities and a network of roads; stressed bravery and honesty
Political Innovations	Established a confederation of city-states	12 tribes were united under one king	King ruled over entire empire and governors over provinces
Economic Activities	Traders and navigators	Herders	Encouraged trade among peoples of the empire

_____

DIRECTIONS: Breaking down a chart into its specific elements or parts will help you in interpreting the chart. Using the preceding chart as a guide, answer the following questions about the elements of a chart.

1. What is the subject of the chart?

Selected Peoples of Ancient Southwest Asia

_____

_____

2. What are the chart's column headings? row labels?

Column headings: Characteristics, Phoenicians, Israelites, Persians;

Row labels: Characteristics, Expansion, Contributions, Political Innovations, Economic Activities

_____

_____

3. Study the data in each column and row. What generalization can you make from the data in the chart?

All civilizations develop economic, governmental, and belief systems.

_____

_____

_____

 # Standardized Test Skills Practice

DIRECTIONS: Use the chart on the previous page to answer the following questions.

1 Which label describes the row that shows cultural or philosophical developments?

   A "Expansion"

  *B "Contributions"

   C "Political Innovations"

   D "Economic Activities"

2 Which of the Southwest Asian peoples represented on the chart were empire builders?

   F only the Israelites

   G only the Phoenicians

   H both the Phoenicians and the Israelites

  *J only the Persians

Standardized Test Skills Practice

ACTIVITY 3
Classifying Facts and Details

Social Studies Objective: The student will identify supporting ideas in a variety of written texts.

A common way to organize information is by **classifying.** It involves sorting or grouping facts and details to general or specific common features. Nearly everything can be classified; most things can be classified in more than one way. When you are faced with a large list of facts and details, think about different sets of common features that are present.

★ Learning to Classify Facts and Details

Use the following guidelines to help you classify facts and details.

- Read and study the information.
- Decide the different categories you will use to group data.

- Sort data into categories and draw conclusions about similarities and differences.

★ Practicing the Skill

DIRECTIONS: Read the selection below and complete the activity that follows.

Religions of Early India

India today is a land of many religions, including Hinduism, Islam, Jainism, Sikhism, Zoroastrianism, Christianity, and Buddhism. However, the two great religions of early India were Hinduism and Buddhism. Both of these faiths shared many beliefs in common, including reincarnation and release from suffering after a perfect life. However, they also had their differences.

Hindus did not trace their religion to a historical founder. Instead, Hinduism developed gradually over the centuries from a variety of beliefs and practices. Although some thinkers emphasized the oneness of the universe, Hindus tended to worship many deities. They taught that deliverance from the cycles of rebirth was possible through fasting, meditation,

and good deeds. They also practiced elaborate rituals of worship and held to a system of ranking that assigned each person his or her place in life.

Buddhists, on the other hand, avoided devotion to deities. They concentrated on a simple adherence to the teachings of their religion's founder, Siddhartha Gautama. Known as the Buddha, or "Enlightened One," Gautama taught that suffering was caused by desire, and that freedom from desire—and the cycle of rebirth— was attained through fasting, self-denial, and meditation.

Buddhists rejected the complex Hindu social system. Instead, they believed that a person's place in life depended on the person, not on the person's birth.

_____

DIRECTIONS: A web is a convenient way to place facts and details in appropriate categories. Using the webs below, classify the major characteristics of Hinduism and Buddhism.

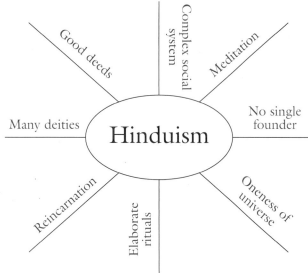

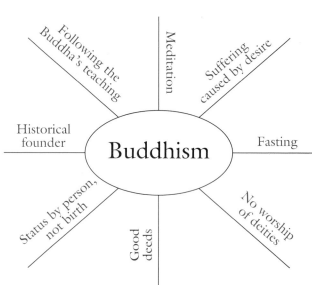

 Standardized Test Skills Practice

DIRECTIONS: Answer the following questions based on the data above.

1 What belief or practice do Hinduism and Buddhism have in common?

   A a person's status based on rank

   *B meditation

   C worship of supernatural beings

   D elaborate rituals by priests

2 Which characteristic below distinguishes Buddhism from Hinduism?

   F belief in reincarnation

   G origins in India

   H emphasis on fasting

   *J a historical founder

Standardized Test Skills Practice

ACTIVITY 4
Identifying the Main Idea

Social Studies Objective: The student will summarize a variety of written texts.

*T*he question "What is this writing about?" is answered in the **main idea.** Every section in the textbooks you read has a main idea. Sometimes titles and headings reveal it. Individual paragraphs are built around a main idea. The rest of the sentences explain, give details about, or support the idea. The main idea is often stated in the **topic sentence** that can be at the beginning, in the middle, or at the end of the paragraph. Sometimes it is implied rather than stated.

★ Learning to Identify the Main Idea

Use the following guidelines to help you identify the main idea.

- Read the selection carefully.
- Look for a specific idea and jot it down in your own words.
- Look for the same idea in a topic sentence. Remember that the topic may be implied.
- Reread the selection to see whether other sentences support the main idea.

★ Practicing the Skill

DIRECTIONS: The following is an excerpt from the *Iliad* by Homer. Read the selection below and complete the activity that follows.

Now the Greeks, with the help of the goddess Athena, decided to play a trick on the Trojans. They built a gigantic wooden horse and pretended it was an offering to the gods. But, secretly, under cover of night, fully armed, inside the wooden horse [were Greek warriors]…

The Trojans stood amazed when they found the horse outside their city gates…They placed wheels under the base of the horse, ropes were stretched about its neck. And while boys and maidens chanted sacred songs, it rolled onward, upward, into Troy…

Meanwhile, night rushed over the city and soon the Trojans lay deep in quiet sleep. At once, the Greek warriors hidden in the horse rushed out and upon the sleeping city. Then, with a braying of trumpets and shouting of men, they rushed through the city with sword and flame.

So fell the ancient city, a queenly city for long years. And the bodies of her children lay scattered in great numbers in the streets.

DIRECTIONS: In searching for the main idea in a reading, you need to distinguish the topic sentence from the other sentences. Using information from the selection on the previous page, fill in the spaces below.

1. Topic sentence:

"Now the Greeks with the help of the goddess Athena, decided to play a trick on the Trojans."

_____

_____

_____

- Detail sentence:

"They built a gigantic wooden horse and pretended it was an offering to the gods."

_____

_____

- Detail sentence:

"Then, with a braying of trumpets and shouting of men, they rushed through the city with sword and flame."

_____

2. Concluding sentences:

"So fell the ancient city, a queenly city for long years. And the bodies of her children lay scattered in great numbers in the streets."

_____

_____

 # Standardized Test Skills Practice

DIRECTIONS: Answer the following questions based on the reading on the previous page.

1 Which of the following sentences best states the main idea of the reading?

   A The goddess Athena opened the gates of Troy for the Greeks.

   B The celebration of the Trojans led to their defeat.

  *C The Greeks devised a scheme to gain entrance into Troy.

   D Many years of warfare had weakened the great city.

2 What sentence below best represents a lesson that can be learned from this excerpt from the *Iliad*?

   F People should celebrate when they receive gifts from their enemies.

   G Hospitality is a good thing to offer both friends and enemies.

  *H It is best to be cautious when your enemy offers you a gift.

   J Celebrating should always take place after a victory.

Standardized Test Skills Practice

ACTIVITY 5
Making Inferences

Social Studies Objective: The student will analyze information in a variety of written texts in order to make inferences and generalizations.

*U*sing diagrams, charts, and other data sources requires careful reasoning skills. Sometimes you may have to draw conclusions based solely on the evidence in the source itself. This is known as making an **inference.** Making an inference involves combining the limited facts at hand and your general knowledge to form a reasonable conclusion.

★ Learning to Make Inferences

Use the following guidelines to help you use data to make accurate inferences.

- Observe the key features and details of the source.
- Decide what general topic is being presented or illustrated.
- Review what you already know about the topic.

- Use logic and common sense to form a conclusion about the topic.
- If possible, find specific information that proves or disproves your inference.

★ Practicing the Skill

DIRECTIONS: Read the paragraph and study the outline below. Then complete the activity that follows.

A Roman Archaeological Dig

The remains of Roman buildings, aqueducts, and roads are found throughout Europe. During the Middle Ages, scholars studied the portions of ruins that could be seen above ground. In the early modern period, the science of archaeology was born. Today, archaeologists use scientific methods and instruments to analyze remains that often lie many feet below the street level of modern cities. Their work is carried out not only in Europe but also throughout the world.

Read the following short outline of their working technique.

I.   Collecting Data
    1. Locating site by satellite, radar, or probes
    2. Laying out a grid
    3. Digging away soil with specialized tools
II. Analyzing Artifacts
    1. Dating artifacts by various methods
    2. Describing and classifying artifacts
III. Synthesizing
    1. Drawing conclusions about artifacts
    2. Making inferences about ancient societies

Name _____ Date _____ Class _____

DIRECTIONS: *Observing details can help you make inferences. Analyze the diagram below that shows an imaginary archaeological dig of Roman ruins. Answer the questions that follow based on this diagram and the information on the previous page.*

Archaeological Dig of Ancient Rome

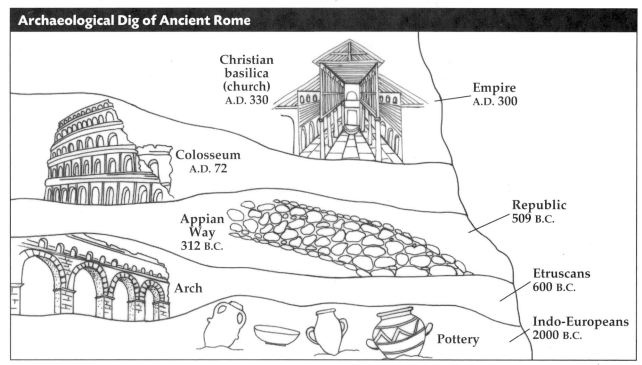

1. What details and key features are shown on the diagram?

   Roman remains—pottery, ruins, buildings (Colosseum, basilica)—with labels and dates

2. What information do you already know about ancient Rome that might help you in drawing conclusions about the diagram?

   Answers will vary, but students might refer to Roman expansion, armies, and rulers.

3. What inferences can you make about ancient Roman society?

   The Romans excelled in engineering, constructing buildings and roads; they also promoted trade.

4. What inferences can you make about the work of archaeologists from both the diagram and the information found on the previous page?

   Answers will vary but should focus on the fact that archaeological work involves developing an

   understanding of the past by analyzing the physical remains of past civilizations.

 # Standardized Test Skills Practice

DIRECTIONS: Answer the following question based on the diagram.

1 What inferences can you make about the Roman world between the time of the Etruscans and the rise of the Empire?

   *A People became wealthier and engaged in building projects.

   B The Romans were conquered by other peoples.

   C Roman rulers fought and lost many wars.

   D The Romans made few advances.

Copyright © by The McGraw-Hill Companies, Inc.

Name _____ Date _____ Class _____

Standardized Test Skills Practice

ACTIVITY 6
Writing About Comparisons and Contrasts

Social Studies Objective: The student will respond appropriately in a written composition to the purpose/audience specified in a given topic.

When you **compare** two or more subjects, you explain how they are similar. When you **contrast** them, you explain how they are different. Writing about comparisons and contrasts, however, involves more than stating similarities and differences. You also explore relationships and draw conclusions.

★ Learning to Write About Comparisons and Contrasts

Use the following guidelines to help you write about comparisons and contrasts.

- Identify or decide what subjects will be compared and contrasted.
- Determine common categories, or areas, in which comparisons and contrasts can be made.
- Look for similarities and differences within these areas.

- Before writing, organize your comparison and contrast by creating a graphic organizer.
- In your writing, you can compare and contrast the subjects category by category, or you may discuss all aspects first of one subject, then those of the others.

★ Practicing the Skill

DIRECTIONS: Read the selection below and complete the activity that follows.

In the late 300s, the Roman Empire split into two parts: an eastern empire with its capital at Constantinople, and the remnants of the old empire in western Europe. The eastern domain, later known as the Byzantine Empire, lasted over 1,000 years. At its height, the Byzantine Empire ruled vast territories in southeastern Europe, Southwest Asia, and North Africa.

North of the Byzantine Empire the Eastern Slavs established a new civilization centered in Kiev on the Dnieper River. It later became the foundation for the modern nations of Russia, Ukraine, and Belarus.

The Eastern Slavs adopted the Eastern Orthodox faith and the Cyrillic alphabet from the Byzantines. They also developed artistic and architectural styles based on Byzantine models.

A third civilization arose in Southwest Asia and became known as the Arab Empire. Shaped by the religion of Islam, the Arab realm eventually stretched from Southwest Asia across North Africa and into the European lands of Spain and the Balkans.

All of these civilizations existed at about the same time period and had contact with each other over many years. Today, their influence continues to affect the peoples of Europe and Southwest Asia.

DIRECTIONS: In preparing to write a comparison and contrast essay, you may find a comparison frame chart particularly useful. To create a comparison frame, write the subjects as headings across the top. Then list on the left side the categories that you will compare and contrast. Finally, list relevant information in the boxes. Below is an example of a comparison frame that compares and contrasts Byzantine, Eastern Slavic, and Islamic civilizations.

	Byzantine Empire **395–1453**	**Eastern Slavs** **980–1472**	**Arab Empire** **c. 632–1258**
Location and Main Cities	• Balkan Peninsula • Constantinople	• North of Black Sea, along river system • Kiev and Moscow	• Arabian Peninsula, other parts of Southwest Asia; North Africa; Balkans • Makkah, Damascus, Jerusalem, Baghdad
Life and Culture	• Women ran households • Artisans produced icons and jewelry	• Women ran households • Artisans produced icons and jewelry	• Women ran households • Artisans produced textiles; calligraphy
Religion	• Eastern Orthodox • Emperor: head of church and state	• Eastern Orthodox (from the Byzantines) • Close union of church and state	• Islam • Establishment of a political-religious community
Government	• Roman law codified into civil law known as Justinian Code • Powerful empire	• Ruled by princes, nobles, and assemblies • Used Justinian Code	• Powerful empire • Rule by caliphs as successors of Muhammad • Law based on Quran
Economy	• Herding, farming • Crossroads for trade between Europe and Asia	• Farming • Center of trade between Black Sea and Scandinavia and western Europe and central Asia	• Herders and farmers in rural areas • Traders in towns on East-West routes from India, Europe, and Africa
Contributions	• Preserved classical philosophy • Developed dome for use in architecture	• Cyrillic alphabet • Used dome and wood in architecture • icon painting	• Algebra • Breakthroughs in astronomy, chemistry, medicine
Decline	• Fell to Ottoman Turks	• Conquered by Mongols; eventual rise of Moscow	• Broken apart into separate states by Turkish and Mongol invaders

Standardized Test Skills Practice

DIRECTIONS: On a separate sheet of paper, write a short composition comparing and contrasting Byzantine, Eastern Slavic, and Arab civilizations. You may organize your material subject by subject, or category by category. At the end of your composition, draw conclusions about the impact of these civilizations on world history.

Standardized Test Skills Practice

ACTIVITY 7
Descriptive Writing About a Visual

Social Studies Objective: The student will respond appropriately in a written composition to the purpose/audience specified in a given topic.

Paintings, illustrations, and photographs are **visual data** that can be useful sources for writing a descriptive composition. **Descriptive writing** tells what something is like. *Good* descriptive writing depends on the effective use of details and the organization of those details into meaningful paragraphs.

★ Learning to Write Descriptively About a Visual

Use the following guidelines to help you write a composition describing a visual.

- Decide what subject the painter or photographer has chosen to portray.
- Study the details of the visual and how they are arranged.
- Think about the central impression created by the visual and how that impression is communicated.

- Write down your thoughts about the visual, directing them to a particular reader or audience.
- Arrange your description of the visual's details in spatial order—that is, left to right—and according to importance.
- Organize details around a topic sentence.

★ Practicing the Skill

DIRECTIONS: Read the selection and study the map below. Then complete the activity that follows.

Ancient Nubia

At about the same time the earliest pharaohs ruled Egypt, another great African society began to develop on the Upper Nile River. This area between the present day cities of Aswan and Khartoum came to be known as Nubia. Even though the Upper Nile does not have the flat, fertile valley of the Lower Nile, the Nubians prospered because of their skill at metal and pottery manufacturing and trading of ebony, ivory, and gold.

Powerful monarchs governed Nubia, which eventually became known as Kush. The Kushite king Piankhi conquered Egypt in 750 B.C. After this victory, Kushite kings ruled their domains from the capital of Napata. The city boasted white sandstone temples, monuments, and pyramids fashioned in styles similar to those of the Egyptians.

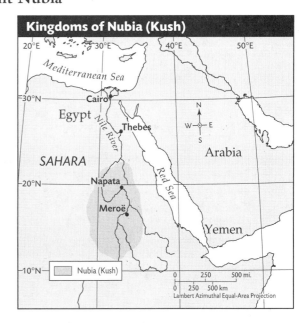

Name _____ Date _____ Class _____

DIRECTIONS: Photographs and paintings provide visual clues about past civilizations. Study this photograph of a wall painting from a Nubian tomb that shows four Nubian princes presenting gold gifts to an Egyptian ruler. Based on your reading of the short introduction on the previous page and your analysis of the wall painting, answer the following questions.

1. What is the painting's subject?

   Nubians presenting gifts to Egyptian ruler

2. What details are shown in the painting?

   wealthy princes with servants, chariot, and gifts

3. How are details in the painting arranged? Why?

   They are arranged as a procession or caravan. Answers will vary but might suggest that the group's arrangement expresses the power and wealth of the princes and their act of paying homage to the ruler.

4. In writing about the painting, what topic sentence would you write?

   Sentences will vary but should focus on the princes and their gift-giving.

 Standardized Test Skills Practice

DIRECTIONS: Imagine that you are a tour guide who shows recent museum acquisitions. This Nubian wall painting is the newest acquisition, and you decide to give a lecture about it to a tour group. On a separate sheet of paper, draft a paragraph that describes the painting, as well as your personal reactions to it.

Paragraphs should be based on the guidelines for the skill and contain a topic sentence with supporting sentences that provide details. Students should also include their personal reactions.

Standardized Test Skills Practice

ACTIVITY 8
Interpreting Diagrams

Social Studies Objective: The student will analyze information in a variety of written texts in order to make inferences and generalizations.

A simplified drawing that shows how something works is called a **diagram.** Some diagrams use arrows to show movement or relationships. For example, the diagram in this activity shows the movement of goods between Asia and Europe.

★ Learning to Interpret a Diagram

Use the following guidelines to help you interpret diagrams.

- Review the diagram's title to find out the subject or concept.
- Study the information on the diagram, noting the direction of the arrows.

- Identify the relationships among the parts of a diagram.

★ Practicing the Skill

DIRECTIONS: Read the selection below and complete the activity that follows.

The Silk Road is the name given to the great caravan routes that linked Asia and Europe during pre-modern times. Trade along these routes actually began before 100 B.C.

The earliest stretch of the route was in the west, ending at Constantinople and other cities in Southwest Asia. The city of Changan in China became the most important trading center at the eastern end point.

The Silk Road was the passageway for products that included silk, jade, and fruit as well as for ideas and art. For example, the Buddhist and Islamic religions came to China by way of the Silk Road.

At its height, the Silk Road was really many roads that split and converged in various places. Caravans along the road passed over and around some of the most forbidding landscapes on earth: hot, dry deserts and cold, rugged mountains.

Nevertheless, people founded settlements around oases and made profits from the passing traders. Kashgar, in western China, became the crossroads of trade along the route.

After the fall of Rome, the Silk Road became increasingly unsafe. Fewer people traveled on it. In the A.D. 1200s and A.D. 1300s, the route was revived under the Mongols. The European explorer Marco Polo may have used the road to travel to China.

Today one can travel the Silk Road and still find evidence of the people, ideas, and goods that traveled its path and transformed a variety of cultures. It is still possible to see how poles and rocks formed the boundaries of the actual thoroughfares over which goods moved throughout many centuries—before ships, trains, buses, and airplanes replaced mules, carts, and packs.

Name _____ Date _____ Class _____

DIRECTIONS: Diagrams and maps together provide insights about historical movement and relationships. Study the map and diagram below and answer the following questions.

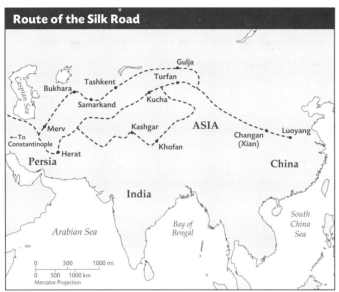

Route of the Silk Road

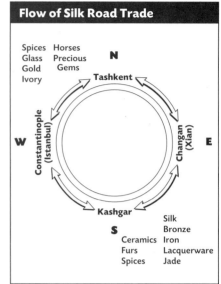

Flow of Silk Road Trade

1. What information is shown in the map and diagram?

   the flow of goods and ideas over the Silk Road

2. What do the arrows indicate?

   the direction in which the trade is moving from east to west, and vice versa

3. How do you think trade along the Silk Road affected the cultures of Asia and Europe?

   Cultural contacts increased through the exchange of ideas and products along the Silk Road.

 # Standardized Test Skills Practice

DIRECTIONS: Answer the following questions based on the data above.

1. Which of the following goods was carried on the Silk Road by caravans from the west?

   *A glass

   B jade

   C ceramics

   D silk

2. What factor do you think had the greatest impact on both Asia and Europe as a result of traders traveling the road to sell their merchandise?

   F Traders using the Silk Road became wealthy and gained political power.

   *G Cultural exchanges in the long run far outweighed the economic benefits of trade.

   H Disputes developed over trade and territory that led to wars.

   J New methods of transportation changed Europe and Asia.

Standardized Test Skills Practice

ACTIVITY 9
Drawing Conclusions

Social Studies Objective: The student will analyze information in a variety of written texts in order to make inferences and generalizations.

A judgment made after thinking about the facts is known as a **conclusion.** To be valid, a conclusion must be supported by logical and factual evidence. Drawing conclusions allows you to understand indirectly stated ideas, so you can apply your knowledge to a wide range of situations. Drawing conclusions is the last step in the process of reasoning.

★ Learning to Draw a Conclusion

Use the following guidelines to help you draw a conclusion.

- Make a list of the important facts or ideas in your reading, visual, or graphic.
- Study the list and ask what more needs to be known.

- Write down several conclusions that explain the meaning of the information.
- Test each conclusion against the facts.

★ Practicing the Skill

DIRECTIONS: Read the paragraph and the excerpt from the Magna Carta below. Then complete the activity that follows.

The Magna Carta, or Great Charter, was a feudal document designed to protect the nobles of England against royal power. However, as time passed, it became a cornerstone of representative government, extending power to many groups in English society in addition to the nobles. The Magna Carta had 63 articles, but only a few are important today. Read the following articles from the document.

The Magna Carta, 1215

38. "No bailiff [officer representing a lord] for the future shall, upon his own unsupported complaint, put any one to his 'law,' without credible witnesses brought for the purpose."

39. "No freeman shall be taken or imprisoned or [dispossessed] or exiled or in anyway destroyed, nor will we go upon him nor send upon him, except by lawful judgment of his peers or by the law of the land."

40. "To no one will we sell, to no one will we refuse or delay, right or justice."

41. "It shall be lawful in the future for any one (excepting always those imprisoned or outlawed in accordance with the law of the kingdom, and natives of any country at war with us, and merchants, who shall be treated as is above provided) to leave our kingdom and to return, safe and secure by land and water, except for a short period in time of war, on grounds of public policy—reserving always the allegiance due to us."

DIRECTIONS: Review the guidelines for drawing conclusions. Reread the four articles from the excerpt of the Magna Carta. Then, research the history of the Magna Carta and its impact on the people of England. Using your knowledge, write one sentence about each article that states its meaning.

Article 38 _A person cannot be brought to justice without witnesses._

_____

_____

Article 39 _No punishment without the judgment of one's peers (social equals)._

_____

_____

Article 40 _Justice cannot be sold; everyone has a right to a fair trial._

_____

_____

_____

Article 41 _Safe departure and return to one's country is guaranteed._

_____

_____

_____

 # Standardized Test Skills Practice

DIRECTIONS: Answer the following questions based on the data above.

1 Considering the structure of feudal society, which of the following groups do you think would not be included in Article 39 of the Magna Carta?

  A knights

  *B serfs

  C barons

  D village priests

2 Why is the Magna Carta one of the most important documents in the rise of representative government?

  *F It distinctly stated the principle that the king is and shall be beneath the law.

  G The barons were given power to control all local government affairs.

  H Freemen were under the control of neither the barons nor their bailiffs.

  J It freed the peasants from the manorial system.

Standardized Test Skills Practice

ACTIVITY 10
Reading a Map Scale

Social Studies Objective: The student will interpret maps to answer geographic questions, infer geographic relationships, and analyze geographic change.

Cartographers draw maps to **scale.** On each map, a measured distance will represent a fixed distance on the earth. For example, one inch on a map may represent 100 miles; however, on another map, one inch might represent 1,000 miles. This relationship, or **scale of distance,** often is shown on a **map scale**—a line with numbers specifying the unit of measurement and the number of miles or kilometers this unit represents. On some maps, the scale appears as a fraction.

★ Learning to Use a Map Scale

Use the following guidelines to measure distances on a map.

- Find the map scale or scale fraction.
- Identify the unit of measurement and the distance that unit represents.
- Using this unit of measurement, measure the

distance between two points on the map.
- Multiply that number by the number of miles or kilometers represented by each unit.

★ Practicing the Skill

DIRECTIONS: Study the map on this page and complete the activity.

There are as many different kinds of maps as there are uses for them. Being able to read a map begins with learning about its parts. The map **key** unlocks the information presented on the map. On this map of Germany, for example, dots mark cities.

On a road map, the key tells what map lines stand for paved roads, dirt roads, and interstate highways. A pine tree symbol may represent a park, while an airplane is often the symbol for an airport.

The **compass rose** is a symbol that tells you where the **cardinal directions**—north, south, east, and west—are positioned on a map. An intermediate direction, such as southeast, may also be on the compass rose. **Intermediate directions** fall between the cardinal directions.

DIRECTIONS: A map scale will often offer two different units of measurement, such as miles and kilometers. Study the map on the previous page to answer the following questions.

1. What is the purpose of a map scale?

A map scale shows how units of measurement on a map correspond proportionally to actual distances on the earth's surface.

2. On the map "Germany: Political," where is the scale located?

The scale is located in the lower left corner of the map.

3. What is the scale of miles on this map?

1/2 inch equals 100 miles

4. Suppose you are a merchant traveling from Munich to Frankfurt. About how far (in miles and kilometers) would you travel from one city to the other?

The distance is about 170 miles, or about 255 kilometers.

5. About how many inches long is the distance between Stuttgart and Dresden? How many miles is this measurement?

1 1/4 inches; 250 miles

 # Standardized Test Skills Practice

DIRECTIONS: Using the map on the previous page, answer the following questions.

1 Bonn is about 150 miles from Nuremberg. What is the approximate distance in kilometers?

  *A about 240 kilometers

  B about 500 kilometers

  C about 600 kilometers

  D about 750 kilometers

2 The distance between Dresden and Hamburg is about 350 kilometers. What is the approximate distance in miles?

  F about 100 miles

  G about 150 miles

  *H about 225 miles

  J about 500 miles

3 In what direction would you travel on a trip from Berlin to Frankfurt?

  A northwest

  *B southwest

  C northeast

  D southeast

4 How much farther is it from Munich to Dresden than from Munich to Stuttgart?

  F about 50 miles

  G about 200 miles

  H about 250 miles

  *J about 100 miles

Name _____ Date _____ Class _____

Standardized Test Skills Practice

ACTIVITY 11
Predicting Outcomes

Social Studies Objecctive: The student will perceive relationships and recognize outcomes in a variety of written texts.

Making accurate **predictions** depends both on gathering reliable facts and on observing past behaviors in similar situations.

★ Learning to Predict Outcomes

Use the following guidelines to help you predict outcomes.

- Review what you already know by listing facts, events, and people's responses. The list will help you recall important events and how they affected people.

- Define and analyze patterns. Try to determine what the patterns show.
- Incorporate your knowledge and observations of similar situations.
- Make a prediction.

★ Practicing the Skill

DIRECTIONS: Read the following selection and complete the activity that follows.

Two Archaeological Treasures

The two finest historical and archaeological sites in the Americas are located high in the Andes of Peru. One of these is Cuzco, the ancient capital of the Inca. Built on the huge rock foundations of earlier civilizations, Cuzco has been named the Archaeological Capital of South America and a Cultural Treasure of Humanity. When the Spanish conquistador Francisco Pizarro first saw Cuzco, he wrote to the king of Spain: "This city is the greatest and finest seen in this country or anywhere in the Indies. We can assure your majesty that it is so beautiful and has such fine buildings that it would be remarkable even in Spain."

The second and even more magnificent site, one which Pizarro never found, is that of Machu Picchu, the abandoned Incan city that was only rediscovered in 1911. Machu Picchu, a Historic National Sanctuary, is so remote that even today it can only be reached by hiking trails and a small

narrow-gauge railroad. Yet many thousands of visitors come each year to view its grandeur and hike the Inca Trail. Situated on top of a mountain and surrounded by terraces for growing crops and aqueducts for water, the houses and temples are built of stone connected by narrow stone walkways. Archaeologists and historians have commented that the masonry was the work of master artisans.

The problem today is that the increasing number of visitors is posing a danger to both Cuzco and Machu Picchu. People damage the ruins by chipping away souvenirs. They also litter the trails and set campfires that get out of control. Extreme weather conditions—excessive rainfall followed by dry spells—also have taken their toll. Erosion has worn away terraces and damaged stone construction. What can be done to protect these priceless areas and yet allow people to enjoy their splendors?

Name _____ Date _____ Class _____

DIRECTIONS: You can develop skills that will help you identify the logical outcomes of decisions or actions. Review the guidelines on the previous page for predicting outcomes. Study the map and photo below. Then answer the following questions about the problems facing many historical sites.

Peru: Historical Monuments

1. Based on the information about the Peruvian sites and on your knowledge of other sites, what factors often pose threats to historic places? Do you notice any patterns? Explain.

   Answers will vary, but students might mention threats posed by climate, urbanization,

   industrial pollution, tourism, remote location, and so on.

2. What steps do you think governments and private groups will take to remedy the problems?

   Answers may mention types of public and private aid, increased educational outreaches, and so on.

 Standardized Test Skills Practice

DIRECTIONS: After reading the selection on the previous page, answer the following questions.

1. The selection gives you reason to believe that the Peruvians will ___

   A ignore the problems faced by Cuzco and Machu Picchu.

   B ban tourists from the historical sites.

   *C take steps to preserve the sites while allowing some tourism.

   D hand the sites over to the United Nations.

2. What clue is given about probable future actions by the Peruvians?

   F They have already built a railroad to discourage hikers.

   *G They have named the sites as a cultural treasure and a national sanctuary.

   H They discourage tourism in the Andes.

   J The residents of Machu Picchu have banned littering.

Standardized Test Skills Practice

ACTIVITY 12
Recognizing Point of View

Social Studies Objective: The student will recognize points of view, propaganda, and/or statements of fact and nonfact in a variety of written texts.

A person's **point of view** is the way in which he or she interprets topics or events. There are a number of factors that affect a person's point of view, including age, gender, ethnic background, and religion. The ability to interpret points of view will help you determine the objectivity of an argument or the accuracy of a description.

★ Learning to Recognize Point of View

Use the following guidelines to help you recognize point of view.

- Read the material and identify the general subject.
- Gather background information on the topic and the author.

- Identify aspects of the topic that the author has emphasized or excluded.
- Identify any words or phrases suggesting a personal opinion.

★ Practicing the Skill

DIRECTIONS: Read the following introduction and excerpt on Leonardo da Vinci. Then answer the questions that follow.

Leonardo da Vinci, an artist who lived from 1452 to 1519, represented the achievements of the Italian Renaissance. A master of painting, sculpture, anatomy, architecture, geometry, and technology, Leonardo was considered a "universal man," one who excelled in many fields of human creativity. In 1550, the noted writer and art critic Giorgio Vasari wrote the following about Leonardo:

Leonardo da Vinci

". . . [Leonardo] practiced not one art only, but all those in which drawing played a part; and having an intellect so divine and marvellous that he was also an excellent geometrician…he made drawing both of ground-plans and other designs of buildings and…suggested the plan of reducing the river Arno to a navigable canal…. Since he wished that his profession should be painting, he studied drawing after nature,…and he executed [his works] in black and white with the point of his brush…. No one has ever equaled him in perfection of finish; and I have one, [a drawing of] a head…, which is divine…. He was continually making models and designs to show men how to

remove mountains with ease, and how to bore them in order to pass from one level to another, and by means of levers, windlasses [hoisting machines], and screws, he showed the way to raise and draw great weights, together with methods for emptying harbors, and pumps for removing water from low places, things which his brain never ceased from devising. Leonardo…began many things and never finished one of them…for the reason that he conceived in ideas difficulties so subtle…that they could never be expressed by the hands, be they ever so excellent."

(Source: Giorgio Vasari, "Life of Leonardo da Vinci," in *Lives of the Most Eminent Painters, Sculptors, and Architects,* 1550)

_____

DIRECTIONS: Identifying point of view helps you determine the accuracy of a description. Review the guidelines for recognizing point of view and answer the following questions.

1. What is the general subject of the Vasari excerpt?

the drawing of Leonardo da Vinci

2. What do you know about Vasari that might reveal his point of view?

Vasari was a noted writer and art critic.

3. What words or phrases indicate his point of view?

"divine and marvellous," "excellent," "perfection of finish," "divine"

4. Based on Vasari's excerpt and the illustrations below that show some of Leonardo's achievements, do you agree or disagree with Vasari's viewpoint? Explain.

Answers will vary but should relate to Leonardo's many-sided talents.

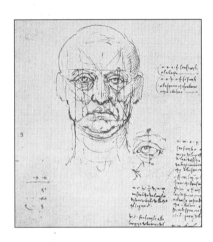 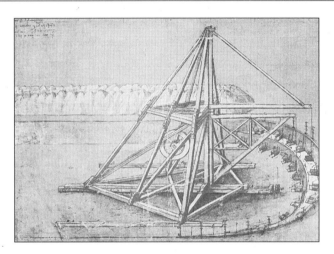

Standardized Test Skills Practice

DIRECTIONS: After reading the excerpt on the previous page, answer the following questions.

1 You can tell from the excerpt that Vasari regarded Leonardo as a ___

  A reformer.

  *B genius.

  C misguided artist.

  D borrower of others' ideas.

2 From the information in the excerpt and the illustrations, which point of view is displayed about Leonardo?

  F Leonardo had no ability to write or to play a musical instrument.

  G Leonardo had no interest in classical scholarship, in philosophy, or in verse.

  H The mysteries of nature were of no interest to Leonardo.

  *J As a man of the Renaissance, Leonardo was interested in all aspects of life.

Standardized Test Skills Practice

ACTIVITY 13
Distinguishing Between Fact and Nonfact

Social Studies Objective: The student will recognize points of view, propaganda, and/or statements of fact and nonfact in a variety of written texts.

Learning to distinguish fact from nonfact can help you make reasonable judgments about what others say. A **fact** is a statement that can be proven by evidence such as records, documents, government statistics, or historical sources. A **nonfact,** often expressed as an opinion, is a statement that may contain some truth but also contains a personal view or judgment.

★ Learning to Distinguish Fact from Nonfact

Use the following guidelines to help you sift facts from nonfacts, or opinions, and to judge the reliability of what you read or hear.

- Identify the facts. Ask yourself the following: Can these statements be proved? Where can I find information to verify them?
- Check the sources for the facts. Reliable sources include almanacs, encyclopedias, and various scholarly works.

- Identify the nonfacts or opinions. Sometimes opinions contain phrases such as *I believe, in my view, it is my conviction, or I think.*
- Identify the purpose. What does the speaker or author want you to believe or do?

★ Practicing the Skill

DIRECTIONS: Read the following information and complete the activity that follows.

Columbus and the Americas

The year 1992 was the 500th anniversary of the arrival of Christopher Columbus in the Americas. Some people saw Columbus's landing as a positive event and celebrated it with festivals and parades. Others, however, viewed the anniversary in a negative light. To them, the arrival of Columbus was the first step in the European conquest and destruction of Native American cultures. Two vastly different viewpoints are expressed below.

Viewpoint A

Columbus's arrival in the Americas was the greatest event in history. I believe it delivered Native American peoples from cultural darkness and brought them the benefits of Europe's magnificent civilization, especially its religion, culture, and technology. As a result of Columbus's landing, two continents provided a home for millions of people from all parts of the globe. American lands produced gold, silver, and new foods, giving European countries even more wealth and power.

Viewpoint B

Columbus's arrival led to a total disaster that forever altered the history of the Americas. In the years after his coming, European explorers and settlers destroyed Native American cultures, killed Native American leaders, and greedily seized Native American lands. The Europeans, believing in the superiority of their own culture, cruelly treated Native Americans, forcing many of them into a form of slavery. Exposed to diseases from Europe for the first time, millions of Native Americans died.

DIRECTIONS: Remember that opinions often include expressions of approval or disapproval, or qualifying phrases. Study the opposing views about the impact of Columbus's voyage. Then answer the following questions.

1. Identify the facts. Is there a way to prove that millions of people from all parts of the globe settled the Americas after Columbus's voyage? Also, did millions of Native Americans die from exposure to diseases from Europe? What could you do to check these and other statements?

Consult works on colonial America written by knowledgeable historians in the field.

_____

_____

2. Notice the nonfacts or opinions. What phrases do the writers sometimes use to signal their own points of view?

Viewpoint A: "greatest event in history," "I believe," "cultural darkness," "Europe's magnificent

civilization"; Viewpoint B: "total disaster," "forever altered," "greedily seized"

_____

3. What is the purpose of each writer? What does each writer want readers to believe?

Writer of Viewpoint A views Columbus's landing as a positive event that brought benefits to the world;

the writer of Viewpoint B believes that Columbus's arrival destroyed Native American cultures and had

a completely disastrous impact on the Americas.

_____

4. How does knowing the purpose of each writer help you distinguish fact and nonfact in their material?

By knowing the author's purpose, you are alerted to any words or phrases that express opinion or bias.

_____

 # Standardized Test Skills Practice

DIRECTIONS: After reading the opposing viewpoints, answer the following questions.

1 Which of the following is an OPINION expressed in the viewpoints?

A Europeans brought their culture and religion to the Americas.

B Millions of Native Americans died from exposure to diseases from Europe.

*C Columbus's arrival was a disaster that totally altered the history of the Americas.

D American lands provided gold, silver, and new foods to Europe.

2 Which of the following statements is a FACT?

*F The Europeans brought their religion to Native Americans.

G Columbus's arrival delivered Native American groups from cultural darkness.

H Columbus's arrival in the Americas was the greatest event in history.

J The Americas provided a new home for Europe's magnificent civilization.

Name _____ Date _____ Class _____

Standardized Test Skills Practice

ACTIVITY 14
Persuasive Writing About an Issue

Social Studies Objective: The student will respond appropriately in a written composition to the purpose/audience specified in a given topic.

A writer uses persuasion to express his or her opinion and to make readers agree with it, change their own opinion, and sometimes take action. Like other types of writing, **persuasive writing** consists of a topic, a main idea about the topic, and supporting details. However, your main purpose in persuasive writing is to influence other people. Therefore, you need to pay special attention to your audience, presenting your supporting ideas in a way that will persuade your audience to accept your opinion.

★ Learning to Write Persuasively

Use the following guidelines to help you write persuasively.

- Direct your argument to a particular audience.
- Present your viewpoint in a main idea statement.
- Support your main idea statement with facts and relevant opinions.

- Use supporting evidence that appeals to both reason and emotion.
- Anticipate and respond to possible opposing viewpoints.
- End by summarizing your ideas and, if appropriate, give a clear call to action.

★ Practicing the Skill

DIRECTIONS: Read the selection below and complete the activity that follows.

King Louis XIV

Louis XIV is recognized as the most powerful king who ever ruled France. His 72-year reign set the style for European monarchies during the 1600s and 1700s.

Although Louis relied on a bureaucracy, he was the source of all political authority in France. Jacques Bossuet, the leading church official of France during the 1600s, supported Louis's feelings about absolute monarchy. Bossuet wrote:

"What grandeur that a single man should embody so much!... Behold this holy power, paternal and absolute, contained in a single head: you see the image of God in the king, and you have the idea of royal majesty."

According to Bousset, subjects had no right to revolt. Kings need account to no one except God, but they should act with humility and restraint because "God's judgment is heaviest for those who command."

DIRECTIONS: Persuasive writing involves the use of facts or opinions that favor one side. Following the guidelines on the previous page, write a persuasive composition on the merits of Louis XIV's reign. Imagine that you are an official in Louis XIV's court or a prominent church official close to the king. On the lines below, defend Louis XIV's system of absolute rule. Your purpose is to convince Louis's opponents in France and in other European countries that he is a good monarch. Use information from your text as well as other sources to support your position.

Students might note the following: Louis set the style for European royalty, government, and society in the late 1600s; he relied on a bureaucracy that provided many jobs for people; his government kept law and order at home and strengthened France's defenses to fight foreigners; the king chose top advisers from the new middle class; he promoted trade and industry through mercantilist policies; he increased the power and glory of France; he encouraged artists and writers.

_____

_____

_____

_____

_____

_____

_____

_____

_____

_____

_____

 # Standardized Test Skills Practice

DIRECTIONS: Imagine that you are an English republican writer or a French Protestant noble of the 1600s. On a separate sheet of paper, write a letter or news article aimed at convincing people that the absolute monarchy of Louis XIV is an unsuitable form of government. Use evidence from your text or other sources to support your argument.

Students might argue that Louis wasted money on his court and built expensive palaces that left France near financial ruin; sold government offices, thereby encouraging corruption; failed to reform France's complicated and unjust tax system; promoted costly wars of expansion that placed burdens on the French people; ended religious toleration and drove talented Huguenots from the country.

Name _____ Date _____ Class _____

Standardized Test Skills Practice

ACTIVITY 15
Taking Notes

Social Studies Objective: The student will organize ideas in a written composition on a given topic.

Writing information in a brief logical manner, or **note taking,** will help you to organize material for a composition. Effective note taking involves more than just writing facts in short phrases. It involves breaking up much of the information into meaningful parts so that it can be understood and remembered.

★ Learning to Take Notes

Use the following guidelines to master the skill of note taking.

- Read the material carefully to identify the main ideas.
- Look for patterns or connections between ideas.
- Decide on a method of note taking. One way to take notes is to use graphic organizers—

time lines, cause-and-effect charts, problem-and-solution charts, webs, and comparison frames—or to list your thoughts and impressions under categories.
- Paraphrase the information in short phrases.

★ Practicing the Skill

DIRECTIONS: Read the selection below and complete the activity that follows.

The Taj Mahal

One of the most fascinating buildings in the world is India's magnificent Taj Mahal, built (1630–48) by Shah Jahan as a symbol of his love for his favorite wife, Mumtaz Mahal, after her death. The Taj Mahal is said by many to be the world's most beautiful structure. A nineteenth-century visitor was so impressed that he said all people in the world should be divided into two groups—those who had seen the Taj and those who had not.

At first sight, the Taj Mahal seems like an apparition. Its marble appears to be blue in the morning, white in the afternoon, and glowing pink at dusk. Inside the building, the tomb of Mumtaz Mahal, also made of white marble, was originally inlaid with jewels.

Even though it exhibits a Persian influence in its perfectly balanced shape, the Taj Mahal is a unique architectural creation of the Moguls, the Muslim dynasty that conquered large areas of India in the 1500s. Some people even think the haystacks in the surrounding fields served as an inspiration for the Taj Mahal's great dome.

Name _____ Date _____ Class _____

_____

DIRECTIONS: To master the skill of note taking, read your material carefully and identify the main ideas. After reading the selection and studying the photo on the previous page, develop a set of notes in preparation for writing a description of the Taj Mahal.

A. To help you in your note taking, first answer the following questions.

1. What is the Taj Mahal?

   a large building in India _____

   _____

2. Who built the Taj Mahal? When was it constructed?

   Mogul ruler Shah Jahan built the Taj Mahal between 1630 and 1648. _____

   _____

3. Why was the Taj Mahal built? What does it symbolize?

   as a tomb for Shah Jahan's wife, Mumtaz Mahal; as a symbol of love _____

   _____

4. What impression has the Taj Mahal made on people? What are your own impressions of the building?

   known for the beauty and elegance of its white marble exterior, especially the great dome; students

   should support their answers and provide their own impressions _____

   _____

B. Develop a set of notes by organizing your ideas about the Taj Mahal under the following categories.

THE TAJ MAHAL

HISTORY	SYMBOLISM	APPEARANCE	IMPRESSIONS
built by Shah Jahan as a	_expression of love_	_white marble; great_	_beauty; elegance;_
tomb for his wife,		_dome; tomb of Mumtaz_	_marble appears to_
Mumtaz Mahal, in		_Mahal inside_	_change color_
the 1600s			

 Standardized Test Skills Practice

DIRECTIONS: On a separate sheet of paper, write a descriptive paragraph about the Taj Mahal. Begin with a topic sentence stating the main idea. Then organize supporting details in order of importance, saving strong, mood-capturing details for the end.

The composition should be based on the reading about the Taj Mahal found on the previous page.

Standardized Test Skills Practice

ACTIVITY 16
Outlining Information for Writing

Social Studies Objective: The student will organize ideas in a written composition on a given topic.

*B*efore writing a paper, you can start to outline the information you have researched. An **outline** is a summary of main points and supporting ideas. Outlining involves the use of a system of numbers and letters to help you organize your material and further focus your research efforts. In addition to helping you put information in a logical order when writing a paper, outlining can also be used as a method of note taking and organizing information you read.

★ Learning to Outline for Writing

Use the following guidelines to help you develop an outline for a paper.

- Organize your material into a few main topics. Use Roman numerals (I., II., III.) to label main heads.
- Decide on subtopic heads. Use capital letters (A., B., C.) for subtopics.
- Under subtopics, place relevant details to elaborate on the subtopic. Use Arabic numerals (1., 2., 3.) for these details.

- An "A." head must always be followed by a "B." head; also, a "1." head must always be followed by a "2." head.
- When you have completed your research, prepare a final version of your outline, showing the organization of your paper.
- Write a sentence or statement expressing the central idea of your paper.

★ Practicing the Skill

DIRECTIONS: Study this partial outline, and then answer the questions that follow.

I. Cambodia
  A. Early History
  B. Khmer Culture
II. Vietnam
  A. Chinese Influences
    1. Confucianism, Daoism, and Buddhism
    2. Government
  B. Traditional Ways of Life
  C. Struggle for Independence
    1. The Trung Sisters
    2. Ngo Quyen
III. Thailand
  A. Sukothai Kingdom
  B. Ayutthaya Kingdom
  C. Buddhism
    1. Religious Practices
    2. The Arts

1. What are the three main topics in this outline?

Cambodia, Vietnam, Thailand

_____

2. If you were to add two facts about Khmer culture, where would you place them? Would you use numbers or letters to label the facts?

Under "B. Khmer Culture"; numbers

_____

DIRECTIONS: Outlining helps you identify main ideas and group together related facts. Using the guidelines on the previous page, outline the information on China, Japan, and Korea found in Chapter 16. The main topics will be "I. China" and "II. Japan and Korea." You add the subtopics and details.

I. China

   A. *The Ming Dynasty*

      1. *Government and Society*

      2. *Foreign Influences*

      3. *The Arts*

      4. *Ming Decline*

   B. *The Qing Dynasty*

      1. *Cultural Contributions*

      2. *Foreign Relations*

      3. *Politics and Economics*

   C. *Daily Life*

      1. *Chinese Family*

      2. *Role of Women*

II. Japan and Korea

   A. *Tokugawa Japan*

      1. *Government*

      2. *Foreign Relations*

      3. *Economic and Social Changes*

      4. *Cultural Contributions*

   B. *Korea*

Standardized Test Skills Practice

DIRECTIONS: On a separate sheet of paper, prepare a working outline for a composition on some aspect of the cultures of East Asia, such as "Buddhism's Impact on Japanese Art" or "Technological Innovations of Early China." Before writing your composition, draft a sentence that describes the topic and your approach to it.

Outlines will vary but should be preceded by a topic sentence.

Name _____ Date _____ Class _____

Standardized Test Skills Practice

ACTIVITY 17
Forming Hypotheses

Social Studies Objective: The student will analyze information and form hypotheses.

An educated guess, or **hypothesis,** is based on evidence that a person has about a situation, a problem, or a puzzle. Forming a hypothesis is a step in the scientific method. To prove or disprove a hypothesis, you must organize and analyze data and draw conclusions that are relevant to the situation.

★ Learning to Make and Test Hypotheses

Use the following guidelines to help you perceive cause-and-effect relationships.

- Observe and ask a detailed question about your observation. Ask questions such as *why, how, where, when, who, which,* and *if.*
- Form a hypothesis by making an educated guess to answer the question.
- Gather and analyze data to prove or disprove your hypothesis.

- Challenge your hypothesis by testing and discarding irrelevant data.
- Modify your conclusion and retest.
- Interpret results and draw conclusions, giving facts to prove or disprove it.

★ Practicing the Skill

DIRECTIONS: Read the selection below and complete the activity that follows.

The Scientific Method

The development of the scientific method swept away all the inaccurate and outmoded ideas of earlier philosophers and scientists. One of the first thinkers to question ancient traditions was the scientist Galileo Galilei. His writings challenged long-held beliefs about the universe that were endorsed by the Church. In 1615 Galileo stated: "I do not feel obliged to believe that the same God who has endowed us with senses, reason, and intellect has intended us to forgo their use."

Two other thinkers responsible for developing the scientific method were Francis Bacon and René Descartes. In their writings, Bacon and Descartes stated that truth must be reached through reason. Bacon claimed that ideas based solely on tradition or unproven facts should be discarded completely. Descartes began his search for knowledge by doubting everything except his own existence. He believed that he had found one self-evident truth in the statement, "I think, therefore I am." Isaac Newton used the scientific method as he studied mathematics and science. He said, "Asking the correct question is half the problem. Once the question is formulated there remains to be found only proof. . . ." The application of the scientific method to understanding the world was probably the most important discovery in the 1600s.

DIRECTIONS: Test each hypothesis to see if it fits the known facts and is reasonable. Based on the selection and your reading of the text, speculate about the steps Isaac Newton might have used to develop his idea about the movement of the planets.

Answers will vary but should follow the steps presented in the guidelines for the skill, i.e. question,

hypothesis, testing, and conclusion. For example:

1. Question: What enables the planets to move as they do?

2. Hypothesis: an invisible force affects them

3. Testing: use of mathematical calculations to determine changing forces or quantities

4. Conclusion: The force of gravity holds the entire solar system in place by keeping the sun and

planets in proper orbits.

 # Standardized Test Skills Practice

DIRECTIONS: Read the paragraphs on the previous page and answer the following questions.

1 Which question might Newton have asked as he developed a hypothesis about gravity?

 *A How does the apple fall from the tree?

 B Where does one find the law of inertia?

 C What prevents the polar ice caps from melting?

 D Why does every action have an opposite reaction?

2 Review the steps in the scientific method. Which of the following steps would you take after modifying your conclusion?

 F Discard unrelated data and modify conclusion.

 G Form a hypothesis, analyze data, and challenge the hypothesis.

 *H Retest, interpret results, and draw conclusions.

 J Ask a question, form a hypothesis, and gather data.

3 The scientific revolution began a slow but profound change in the way people viewed and studied the world. Which of the following expresses one of the major effects of the scientific revolution?

 *A The scientific revolution began to erode beliefs in magical spells, witch craft, and astrology.

 B The scientific revolution had an immediate impact on agriculture and medicine.

 C The scientific revolution created wealth and power for many scientists and thinkers.

 D The scientific revolution was a major cause of social revolutions that followed it.

Standardized Test Skills Practice

ACTIVITY 18
Making Generalizations

Social Studies Objective: The student will analyze information in a variety of written texts in order to make inferences and generalizations.

A broad statement drawn from a group of facts about a topic is called a **generalization.** To be valid, a generalization must be supported by evidence that is logical and factual. Learning to make generalizations will help you develop conclusions and identify trends. An example of a generalization is "Only tall people play basketball well." Can this be supported by facts? If not, it is not a valid generalization.

★ Learning to Make Generalizations

Use the following guidelines to help you perceive cause-and-effect relationships.

- Collect facts about a topic.
- Classify the facts into categories.
- Identify the relationships among the facts.
- Make a generalization that states a relationship and is consistent with most of the supporting facts.

- Write a paragraph using the generalization and its supporting facts.
- Examine how your generalization relates to cause-and-effect relationships.

★ Practicing the Skill

DIRECTIONS: Read the paragraphs below and complete the activity that follows.

The Age of Revolutions

From the 1600s to the 1800s, people in the Western world lived through a time of great political and social revolutions. The two most important ideas behind these revolutions were democracy, the right of people to take an active part in government, and nationalism, the right of people who share a common culture to have their own nation. In some countries, people influenced by the new ideas rebelled against monarchs in the hope of winning freedom and creating more just societies. Although in some cases these revolutions were largely successful, in other cases the supporters of freedom and justice did not achieve many of their original goals.

During the 1700s, worsening relations between Great Britain and the North American colonies led to the American Revolution. Following the Revolutionary War, the newly independent states ratified the Constitution of the United States in 1788. This document established the framework for a federal republic and later provided a Bill of Rights that protected personal liberties.

The American Revolution influenced the people of France, who became increasingly critical of their absolute monarchy. In 1789, social injustice, economic distress, and ideas of liberty combined to spark the French Revolution. During the 25 years that followed, revolutionary changes led France from a constitutional monarchy to a democratic republic and, finally, to a military dictatorship.

Name _____ Date _____ Class _____

DIRECTIONS: Generalizations are made from individual, supporting facts. Study the chart below. Then formulate a generalization about the American and French Revolutions. You can use the information on the chart and your own knowledge of the revolutions. Choose to focus on leaders, goals, events, or outcomes. Write your sentences on a separate sheet of paper.

American Revolution	French Revolution
No fixed system of social classes	Rigid system of social classes
Belief in Enlightenment values, such as natural rights	Belief in Enlightenment values, such as natural rights
Opposition to monarchy; support for a republic	Opposition to monarchy; support for a republic
Tradition of limited government	Tradition of strong, central authority
Experience in self-government through colonial legislatures	Little experience in self-government by popular assemblies
Colonial revolt against parent country with a constitutional monarchy	Revolt against a national absolute monarchy
Relative cooperation among social groups	Social upheaval and struggle among classes
Leaders were practical thinkers as well as visionaries.	Some leaders supported terror or war to achieve sweeping revolutionary goals.

Standardized Test Skills Practice

DIRECTIONS: Answer the following questions based on the reading and the chart.

1 Which of the following characteristics related to both the American and French Revolutions?

  A bloody conflict between different social classses

  *B ideas influenced by Enlightenment thinkers

  C creation of stable republic with checks and balances

  D tradition of absolute monarchy

2 Based on the chart, what generalization can you make about revolutions?

  F Revolutions rarely accomplish their goals.

  *G Political revolutions are easier to accomplish if there is no accompanying social revolution.

  H Revolutions have a better chance of success if visionary leaders insist on perfection.

  J People living in countries with rigid political and social systems are likely to revolt.

Standardized Test Skills Practice

ACTIVITY 19
Interpreting Graphs

Social Studies Objective: The student will express or solve problems using mathematical representation.

     Drawings that present statistical data are known as **graphs.** Each kind of graph has certain advantages in presenting numerical facts. Line graphs are best for showing how statistics change over time. Bar graphs are better for comparing numbers over time. Circle graphs show relationships among parts of a whole.

★ Learning to Interpret Graphs

Use the following guidelines to help you interpret graphs.

- Read the graph's title.
- Read data on the axes of bar graphs, follow the dots/lines on a line graph, or read the

    labels for each segment in a circle graph.
- Analyze the data, make comparisons, and draw conclusions.

★ Practicing the Skill

DIRECTIONS: Study the map, bar graph, and table below to discover population changes in Great Britain during the Industrial Revolution.

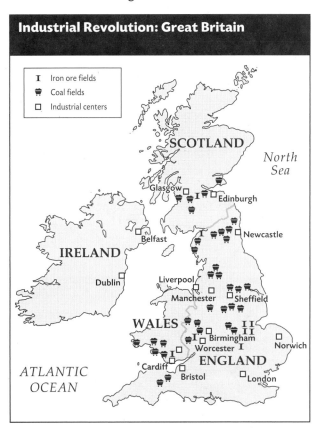

Industrial Revolution: Great Britain

Legend:
- I Iron ore fields
- Coal fields
- □ Industrial centers

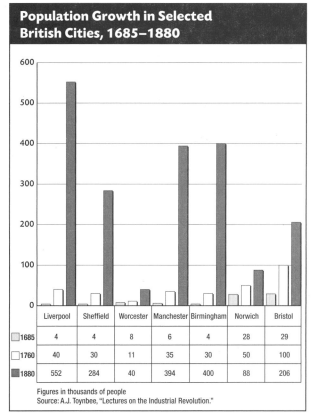

Population Growth in Selected British Cities, 1685–1880

	Liverpool	Sheffield	Worcester	Manchester	Birmingham	Norwich	Bristol
1685	4	4	8	6	4	28	29
1760	40	30	11	35	30	50	100
1880	552	284	40	394	400	88	206

Figures in thousands of people
Source: A.J. Toynbee, "Lectures on the Industrial Revolution."

Name _____ Date _____ Class _____

DIRECTIONS: Use the information on the bar graph and table on the previous page to make a line graph in the space provided below. On a line graph, numbers usually appear on the vertical axis, while time is usually shown on the horizontal axis. Lines on the graph show whether the numbers go up or down over time. On your line graph, show population changes that occurred in British cities over time. Place a title on the horizontal axis. Select and compare two cities, using two lines of different colors. Then draw conclusions about the impact of the Industrial Revolution on these cities.

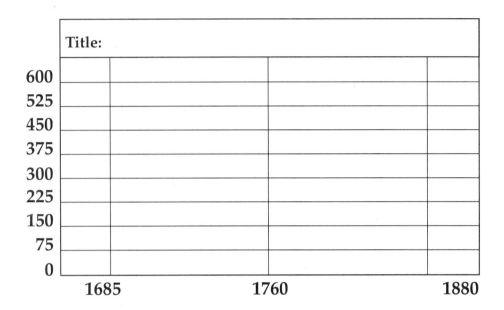

Figures in thousands of people

Students should base their line graphs on the data from the bar graph, table, and map on the previous page.

 # Standardized Test Skills Practice

DIRECTIONS: Analyze the bar graph and table on the previous page, and answer the following questions.

1 Which industrial city grew the most from 1685 to 1880?

  *A Liverpool

  B Sheffield

  C Manchester

  D Birmingham

2 According to the statistics on the graph and chart, what was the population of Birmingham in 1880?

  F 600,000

  G 550,000

  *H 400,000

  J 200,000

Standardized Test Skills Practice

ACTIVITY 20
Writing About a Political Cartoon

Social Studies Objective: The student will respond appropriately in a written composition to the purpose/audience specified in a given topic.

*E*xpressions of opinion are often presented visually in the form of **political cartoons.** Using caricature and symbols, political cartoons help readers see relationships and draw conclusions about personalities and events.

★ Learning to Write About a Political Cartoon

Use the following guidelines to help you write about political cartoons.

- Determine the main theme or subject of the cartoon.
- Find out what the cartoon's caricatures and symbols represent.
- Identify the issues that are addressed.

- Write a topic sentence based on the information you have gathered.
- Use supporting ideas to clarify the relationships among the cartoon's figures and symbols.
- Draw conclusions about the cartoonist's point of view.

★ Practicing the Skill

DIRECTIONS: Read the paragraphs below and complete the activity that follows.

The Communist Manifesto

The German thinkers Karl Marx and Friedrich Engels called on the workers of the world to unite in revolt against the capitalist and aristocratic ruling classes. In their pamphlet *The Communist Manifesto* (1848), they appealed: "Let the ruling classes tremble at a Communist revolution. The proletarians [workers] have nothing to lose but their chains. They have a world to win. Working men of all countries, unite!" According to Marx and Engels, all history has been characterized by class struggles. In recent times, they declared, the owners of factories had exploited workers. Marx and Engels believed that conflict between property owners

and propertyless workers would continue until capitalism was destroyed. Their ideal was a society in which all goods would be held in common and all people would be equal.

History, however, did not proceed by Marx's plan. By 1900 conditions had improved for many western European workers. Some workers continued to favor public control of industry but used democratic means to achieve their goals. The first Marxist revolution took place in Russia, a largely agricultural society. There Marxist revolutionaries shunned democratic values and used force to win power and impose their beliefs on the Russian people.

DIRECTIONS: For special effect, cartoonists often exaggerate a person's physical features or appearance. Their representations can be positive or negative, depending on their point of view. Study the political cartoon below and answer the questions that follow.

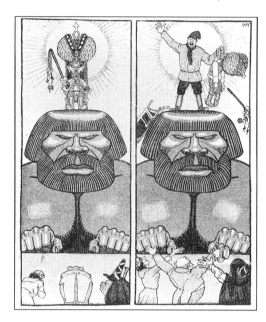

1. What is the theme of the cartoon?

    the power of the peasants and the workers in overthrowing the ruling classes

    _____

2. What do the cartoon's figures and symbols represent?

    The large bearded figure represents the peasantry; the figure with the cap stands for the workers;

    the crowned figure is a monarch representing the old order; the figures at the bottom represent social

    classes bowing before and later, freed from the old order.

    _____

3. What is the cartoonist's interpretation of Marx's theory of class struggle?

    The common people are tired of serving the old order and will rebel.

    _____

4. Is the cartoonist supporting or opposing Marx's viewpoint? Explain.

    supporting Marx's theories: students should provide explanations for their answers

    _____

 Standardized Test Skills Practice

DIRECTIONS: On a separate sheet of paper, write a composition about the political cartoon based on your analysis above. Develop a topic sentence, provide supporting ideas, and end with a conclusion.

In their compositions, students should follow the skill guidelines for writing about political cartoons.

Standardized Test Skills Practice

ACTIVITY 21
Interpreting Primary Sources

Social Studies Objective: The student will summarize a variety of written texts.
Social Studies Objective: The student will respond appropriately in a written composition to the purpose/audience specified in a given topic.

Original records of events made by eyewitnesses are known as **primary sources.** Primary sources include letters, journals, autobiographies, legal documents, drawings, photographs, maps and other objects made at the time. Each primary source can give some, but not necessarily all, kinds of information about an event. For example, a letter from an immigrant to another country might tell about the difficult journey but will not tell how many people immigrated.

★ Learning to Interpret Primary Sources

Use the following guidelines to help you identify primary sources.

- Determine the origins of the source, the source's author, and when and where the source was written.
- Analyze the data for the main idea or concept as well as supporting ideas.

- Learn what data is provided and what data is missing or needed for a full understanding of the concept.
- Consider the author's personal beliefs and attitudes.

★ Practicing the Skill

DIRECTIONS: Read the following selection and complete the activity that follows.

The Age of Imperialism

The term *imperialism* means a country's domination of the political, economic, and social life of another country. By the end of the 1800s, a handful of European countries, together with the United States, carried out policies of imperialism through which they controlled nearly the entire world. Not surprisingly, the era between 1800 and 1914 has come to be called the Age of Imperialism.

The imperialism of the 1800s and early 1900s resulted in three key developments. First, nationalism prompted rival nations to build empires in their quests for power. Second, the Industrial Revolution created a tremendous demand in the West for raw materials and new markets. Finally, feelings of cultural and racial

superiority inspired Western peoples to impose their cultures on distant lands.

Imperial powers built roads, railroads, ports, and urban centers in the overseas lands they acquired. They also set up schools, health clinics, and hospitals. However, many ruling nations took advantage of their colonies by exploiting natural resources without providing economic benefits for most of the people.

The relentless pursuit of colonies and foreign trade by the Western powers heightened international tensions during the late 1800s and early 1900s. In 1914, this growing rivalry contributed to the outbreak of World War I. This conflict heralded the end of the imperial era and Europe's dominant role in world affairs.

DIRECTIONS: The following primary sources deal with the concept of imperalism as it was practiced during the late 1800s and early 1900s. Study the sources and answer the question that follows each one.

Primary Source A

Much has been given to us, and much will rightfully be expected from us. We have duties to others and duties to ourselves, and we can shirk neither.

We have become a great nation, forced by the fact of its greatness into relations with other nations of the earth, and we must behave as beseems a people with such responsibilities. Toward all other nations, large and small, our attitude must be one of cordial and sincere friendship.

We must show not only in our words, but in our deeds, that we are earnestly desirous of their good will by acting toward them in a spirit of just and generous recognition of all their rights. But justice and generosity in a nation, as in an individual, count most when shown not by the weak but by the strong. While ever careful to refrain from wrongdoing others, we must be no less insistent that we are not wronged ourselves…No weak nation that acts manfully and justly should ever have cause to fear us, and no strong power should ever be able to single us out as a subject for insolent aggression.

Source: Theodore Roosevelt's Inaugural Address, March 4, 1904

1. How does Roosevelt see the role of the United States in a world dominated by imperialism?

The United States should respect the rights of all nations, but at the same time it should not allow itself to be "pushed around."

Primary Source B

The American continents, by the free and independent condition which they have assumed, are henceforth not to be considered as subjects for future colonization by any European powers.

Source: James Monroe, Annual Message to Congress, 1823

1. How could this early statement be used against European imperialism?

It could be used to block the spread of European imperialism in the Americas.

 ## Standardized Test Skills Practice

DIRECTIONS: On a separate sheet of paper, write a composition that summarizes the major ideas of Primary Sources A and B. Then, state your point of view on the Age of Imperialism.

Answers will vary but might point out that Westerners mixed idealism and self-interest in their imperialist policies. Students should also explain and defend their own points of view.

Standardized Test Skills Practice

ACTIVITY 22
Forming Hypotheses

Social Studies Objective: The student will analyze information and form hypotheses.

An educated guess, or **hypothesis,** is based on evidence that a person has about a situation, a problem, or a puzzle. Forming a hypothesis is a step in the scientific method. To prove or disprove a hypothesis, you must organize and analyze data and draw conclusions that are relevant to the situation.

★ Learning to Make and Test Hypotheses

Use the following guidelines to help you make and test hypotheses.

- Observe and ask a detailed question about your observation. Ask questions such as *why, how, where, when, which,* and *if.*
- Form a hypothesis by making an educated guess to answer the question.
- Gather and analyze data to prove or disprove your hypothesis.

- Challenge your hypothesis by testing and discarding irrelevant data.
- If necessary, modify your conclusion and retest.
- Interpret results and draw conclusions, using facts to prove or disprove it.

★ Practicing the Skill

DIRECTIONS: Read the selection below and complete the activity that follows.

Earthquakes in Japan

On January 17, 1995, a 7.5-magnitude earthquake struck central Japan, demolishing the city of Kobe, the country's second-largest port. Within minutes the quake triggered landslides and raging firestorms. More than 6,000 people were killed, another 250,000 were made homeless, and the city experienced nearly $120 billion in damage. The quake was the worst to hit Japan in seven decades.

Japan lies in a region where three huge plates of the earth's surface crunch against one another. The collisions are continuous, accounting for the thousands of earthquakes that are part of Japan's geological makeup.

Most of the quakes are short tremors. Every few years, however, a serious quake occurs. Major crunches usually cause several other natural catastrophes, such as landslides and tsunamis (tidal waves).

DIRECTIONS: Based on your knowledge and the reading, speculate about how the frequency and intensity of earthquakes in Japan affect daily life. Follow the steps listed below to formulate and test a hypothesis.

1. Ask a detailed question.

Answers will vary but might include - Question: What precautions do people have to take in their everyday lives to prepare for earthquakes?

2. State a hypothesis about possible answers to your question.

Answers will vary but might include - Hypothesis: Construct buildings that will withstand earthquake tremors to the greatest degree possible.

3. Propose a test for your hypothesis to see if it fits the known facts and is correct.

Answers will vary but might include - Testing: Compare houses and buildings in Japan that have been constructed using various quake-proof techniques to those that use older techniques and to buildings in other earthquake-prone areas of the world.

4. State a conclusion about whether your hypothesis was correct.

Answers will vary but might include - Conclusion: Zoning and construction codes that require earthquake-proof building techniques increase the likelihood that homes and buildings will be able to withstand an earthquake.

 Standardized Test Skills Practice

DIRECTIONS: Read the paragraphs on the previous page and answer the following questions.

1 Which of the following is a reasonable hypothesis about how earthquakes affect the Japanese?

A Most Japanese people give little thought to the dangers of earthquakes.

B Most Japanese people believe that earthquakes are too unpredictable to require special construction techniques.

*C Over the years, Japanese builders have developed techniques to make homes and public buildings more earthquake-safe.

D Many Japanese people have crowded into cities for safety from earthquakes.

2 A Japanese scientist hypothesized that traditional wooden houses are more earthquake-safe than houses made from other building materials. Which of the following would be the most reasonable and accurate way to test that hypothesis?

F Study the number of injuries and deaths in Kobe of people who lived in wooden houses compared to people in houses made of other materials.

G Take an opinion poll of a representative sample of Japanese people on which type of house they prefer.

*H Observe how wooden houses hold up against other natural disasters, such as floods and volcanic eruptions.

J Wait for the next earthquake in Japan to make a count of injuries and deaths.

Name _____ Date _____ Class _____

Standardized Test Skills Practice

ACTIVITY 23
Making Decisions

Social Studies Objective: The student will perceive relationships and recognize outcomes in a variety of written texts.
Social Studies Objective: The student will respond appropriately in a written composition to the purpose/audience specified in a given topic.

In problem solving, a choice made among two or more alternative courses of action is known as a **decision.** Your final decision should not conflict with your goals or values, so you must weigh each choice carefully.

★ Learning to Make a Decision

Use the following guidelines to help you make a decision.

- Find out what issue requires a decision.
- List the alternative decisions available to you.
- Identify the positive and negative consequences of each choice.

- Evaluate each choice and its consequences in light of your goals and values.
- Make a decision and put it into effect.

★ Practicing the Skill

DIRECTIONS: Study the following statements of American foreign policy, then complete the activity that follows.

Washington's Farewell Address, September 17, 1796

"Why, by interweaving our destiny with that of any part of Europe, entangle our peace and prosperity in the toils of European ambition, rivalship, interest, humor, or caprice? It is our true policy to steer clear of permanent alliances with any portion of the foreign world…"

Wilson's Appeal for Neutrality, August 19, 1914

"The effect of the war upon the United States will depend upon what American citizens say and do. Every man who really loves America will act and speak in the true spirit of neutrality, which is the spirit of impartiality and fairness and friendliness to all concerned…. Some will wish one nation, others another, to succeed in the momentous struggle…. Such divisions…might seriously stand in the way of the proper performance of our duty as the one great nation at peace, the one people holding itself ready to play a part of impartial mediation and speak the counsels of

peace and accommodation, not as a partisan, but as a friend.

U.S. Response May 13, 1915

"In view of recent acts of the German authorities in violation of American rights on the high seas which culminated in the torpedoing and sinking of the British steamship *Lusitania* on May 7, 1915, …it is clearly wise and desirable that the Gorverment of the United States and the Imperial German Government should come to a clear and full understanding as to the grave situation which has resulted." *(Note to German Ambassador written by Woodrow Wilson)*

Wilson's Address to Congress April 19, 1916

"[I]f it is still its purpose to prosecute relentless and indiscriminate warfare against vessels of commerce by the use of submarines…the Government of the United States is at last forced to the conclusion that there is but one course it can pursue...but to sever diplomatic relations with the Government of the German Empire altogether."

January 19, 1917
The Zimmerman Note

(from the German Foreign Secretary to the German Ambassador in Mexico) Berlin, January 19, 1917 "[W]e intend to begin submarine warfare unrestricted. In spite of this, it is our intention to endeavor to keep neutral the United States of America. If this attempt is not successful, we propose an alliance on the following basis with Mexico: That we shall make war together and together make peace. We shall give general financial support, and it is understood that Mexico is to reconquer the lost territory in New Mexico, Texas, and Arizona." *(The Zimmerman Note was intercepted and published on March 1, 1917. The United States declared war on April 8, 1917.)*

DIRECTIONS: Making decisions involves weighing the costs and benefits that each course of action may bring. Imagine that you are U.S. President Woodrow Wilson in the spring of 1917. Should the United States become involved in a conflict 3,000 miles away? Use the preceding sources and your text to answer the following questions.

1. Before the early 1900s, what was the traditional foreign policy of the United States?

The United States sought to avoid any permanent alliances with foreign powers.

2. How did events from 1914 to 1917 change this policy?

The United States became actively involved in World War I after German violation of

American rights of neutrality.

3. On a separate sheet of paper, write a persuasive composition stating the possible alternatives to war that the United States had in 1914 to 1917. If you were President Wilson, what decision would you make? In your writing, include the positive and negative consequences of the action.

Answers will vary, but students should focus on the close cultural and economic ties between the United States and Europe, and the influence and peacemaking capabilities of the United States.

 # Standardized Test Skills Practice

DIRECTIONS: After completing the activity, answer the following questions.

1 What actions of Germany in 1915 and 1916 caused official American protests?

   A invasions of other European nations

   *B violations of American rights on the high seas

   C German efforts to win allies in Asia

   D German infringement of the civil rights of Belgians

2 What additional action by Germany in 1917 helped bring the United States into the war?

   *F German efforts to win Mexican support

   G German agreements with Russia and France

   H German invasion of Belgium and violation of European treaties

   J German submarine attacks and terrorist activity in the Americas

Standardized Test Skills Practice

ACTIVITY 24
Identifying and Evaluating Evidence

Social Studies Objective: The student will analyze information in a variety of written texts in order to make inferences and generalizations.
Social Studies Objective: The student will recognize points of view, propaganda, and/or statements of fact and nonfact in a variety of written texts.

Any information that proves a claim or a conclusion is known as **evidence.** There are four basic kinds of evidence: **oral accounts** (eyewitness testimony), **written documents** (diaries, letters, books, articles), **objects** (artifacts), and **visual forms** (photographs, videotapes, paintings, drawings). These kinds of evidence fall into one of two categories—primary evidence and secondary evidence. Participants or eyewitnesses to events produce **primary evidence. Secondary evidence** is produced later by those who did not experience the events directly.

★ Learning to Identify and Evaluate Evidence

Use the following guidelines to help you identify and evaluate evidence.

- Clearly define the issue, claim, or conclusion.
- Use sources to support or disprove a conclusion.
- Compare the evidence to see if they agree.
- Rate the evidence on objectivity or bias.

★ Practicing the Skill

DIRECTIONS: Read the claim and study the photo and textbook evidence below about the 1930s Dust Bowl. Then complete the activity that follows.

Claim: **The Dust Bowl was an ecological and human catastrophe.**

On Sunday, April 14, 1935, one of the biggest dust storms of this century swept over the Great Plains of the United States. Huge black clouds of dust, more than 1,000 feet high, formed a wall miles wide. Birds flew frantically trying to escape suffocation in the roiling storm. Motorists were stranded for hours along the highway, totally blinded by the impenetrable cloud. The rain sent mud balls splattering to the ground. Dust from the "black blizzard" piled up on railroad lines, and it took snowplows several days to clear the tracks.

Name _____ Date _____ Class _____

DIRECTIONS: Evidence that is interpreted the same way by all observers must be given more consideration than evidence that is less definite. Use the following evidence to support or disprove a claim.

1. In addition to the selection and photo on the previous page, study the map and the John Steinbeck reading below.

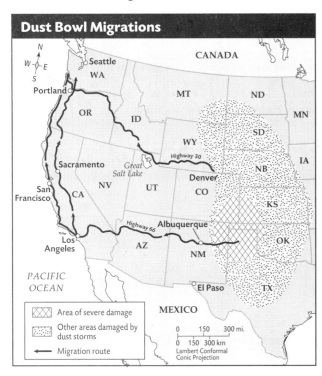

Dust Bowl Migrations

Key:
- Area of severe damage
- Other areas damaged by dust storms
- ← Migration route

0   150   300 mi.
0 150 300 km
Lambert Conformal Conic Projection

"And then the dispossessed were drawn west —from Kansas, Oklahoma, Texas, New Mexico; from Nevada and Arkansas families, tribes, dusted out, tractored out. Carloads, caravans, homeless, and hungry; twenty thousand and fifty thousand and a hundred thousand and two hundred thousand. They streamed over the mountains, hungry, restless—restless as ants, scurrying to find work to do—to lift, to push, to pull, to pick, to cut—anything, any burden to bear, for food. The kids are hungry. We got no place to live. Like ants scurrying for work, for food, and most of all for land."

Grapes of Wrath, John Steinbeck, 1939

2. On the following lines, provide data supporting the claim that the Dust Bowl was an ecological and human catastrophe. Beside the data, list the types of evidence used to support your data.

Ecological: blizzards, devastation of land; textbook, map, Steinbeck reading

Human: loss of work, hunger, migrations; textbook, photo, map, Steinbeck reading

 # Standardized Test Skills Practice

DIRECTIONS: After completing the activity, answer the following questions.

1 Which of the following pieces of evidence is a secondary source?

A the photograph of the migrant family

*B the excerpt from a textbook

C the description by John Steinbeck

D a 1930s newspaper article about the migration

2 Which of the following pieces of evidence is a primary source?

F the excerpt from a textbook

G a recent map of the Dust Bowl area

*H a letter from a migrant family

J a historical account written in the 1990s

Standardized Test Skills Practice

Activity 25
Writing to Inform an Audience

Social Studies Objective: The student will respond appropriately in a written composition to the purpose/audience specified in a given topic.

Writing that involves imparting information to an audience is called **informative,** or **expository,** writing. This kind of writing may include giving directions, presenting a new idea, comparing one thing to another, or explaining how to do something. Knowing your audience—its interests, background, and vocabulary—will help you focus your writing and choose details.

★ Learning to Write Effectively for an Audience

Use the following guidelines to help you write informational material.

- Identify your audience. Consider its interests and background. Use language that your readers will understand.
- Support your main ideas with interesting details that will help readers grasp unfamiliar

information or relate information to their own experiences.
- Use facts, statistics, or quotations to help readers understand the importance of the topic.

★ Practicing the Skill

DIRECTIONS: Read the selection below and complete the activity that follows.

The Zapatistas

Although Mexico won its independence from Spain in 1821, life was hard for the Mexican masses, made up mostly of poor, landless peasants. In 1911, after years of dictatorship, the Mexican people overthrew their leader, Porfirio Díaz. Several revolutionary leaders then vied for power. One was Emiliano Zapata, who led a group of peasants and workers called the Zapatistas.

Proudly wearing the white pants and white shirts that marked them as farm laborers, and shouting "Land and Liberty!" the Zapatistas swept from estate to estate. When a landowner held out, Zapata's anger could not be held back. Once inside, his men would destroy the entire

estate, burning buildings and crops. Whenever a landowner surrendered, Zapata would take the estate and divide the land among the peasants. He was regarded as a true champion of the peasants' right to own the land on which they labored.

In 1919, Zapata died violently at the hands of his enemies. However, the ideals for which he fought lived on and shaped the course of Mexican history. Gradually, the goals of Mexico's revolution began to be realized through law instead of conflict. Although the Mexican Revolution did not end poverty and illiteracy, it did bring political stability, economic progress, and a measure of social justice.

Name _____ Date _____ Class _____

José Clemente Orozco, *Zapatistas,* 1931

1. What details reveal that these people are peasants?

   styles of dress, physical appearance
   _____

2. What detail indicates that the peasants are prepared for violence?

   some are carrying weapons
   _____

3. What concept or idea does Orozco present in the mural?

   The revolutionary movement of Mexico's peasants cannot be stopped.
   _____

 Standardized Test Skills Practice

DIRECTIONS: Look carefully at the Orozco mural above and read the title. On a separate sheet of paper, write a short informative essay describing what is happening in the picture. Your audience is a group of students unfamiliar with the Mexican Revolution. Before writing, think about what your audience needs to know and how you can relate your information to their experiences.

Answers will vary but should focus on the social conflicts in turn-of-the-century Mexico and the rise of a revolutionary movement to achieve some kind of justice.

Standardized Test Skills Practice

ACTIVITY 26
Recognizing Forms of Propaganda

Social Studies Objective: The student will recognize points of view, propaganda, and/or statements of fact and nonfact in a variety of written texts.

*I*n contrast to the scientific method that is based on factual evidence, **propaganda** aims to persuade people to accept a viewpoint that may be good or bad. Through appeals to the emotions, propaganda attempts to force the public to accept a particular viewpoint without careful reflection. Both the Axis and Allies in World War II used propaganda.

★ Learning to Recognize Propaganda

Use the following guidelines to help you recognize propaganda.

- Look for emotion-filled words.
- Identify various techniques of propagandists.
- Find out who is the target for propaganda.

- Draw conclusions about the use of propaganda to unite and motivate.

★ Practicing the Skill

DIRECTIONS: Read the following selection, study the poster, and complete the activity.

The Use of Propaganda in War Time

"Guns, tanks, and bombs were the principal weapons of World War II, but there were other, more subtle, forms of warfare as well. Words, posters, and films waged a constant battle for the hearts and minds of the American citizenry just as surely as military weapons engaged the enemy. Persuading the American public became a wartime industry, almost as important as the manufacturing of bullets and planes. The Government launched an aggressive propaganda campaign to galvanize public support, and some of the nation's foremost intellectuals, artists, and filmmakers became warriors on that front."

(Source: Introduction to "Powers of Persuasion" Exhibit, National Archives Building, Washington, D.C.)

During World War II, the most effective propaganda posters were those that made a direct, eye-catching appeal.

Name _____ Date _____ Class _____

DIRECTIONS: Propaganda appeals to people's hopes, fears, and biases. Read the following statements made by Adolf Hitler and Winston Churchill. Answer the questions below that relate to propaganda during World War II.

Adolf Hitler

The victor will not be asked afterward whether he told the truth or not. In starting and waging a war it is not right that matters, but victory. Close your hearts to pity! Act brutally! Eighty million people must obtain what is their right....The stronger man is right....Be harsh and remorseless! Be steeled against all signs of compassion! Whoever has pondered over this world order knows that its meaning lies in the success of the best means of force..."

Winston Churchill

"We have before us an ordeal of the most grievous kind. You ask, what is our policy? I will say: it is to wage war against a monstrous tyranny, never surpassed in the dark, lamentable catalogue of human crime. That is our policy. You ask, what is our aim? I can answer with one word: Victory – victory at all costs, victory in spite of terror, victory, however long and hard the road may be; for without victory, there is no survival."

1. What is the general purpose of propaganda?

to use selective information and emotional appeals to win support for a position

2. What emotionally charged words, phrases and visual images do you find in the two statements above?

Hitler's use of harsh, aggressive language: "Act brutally!", "Be harsh and remorseless," and so on;

Churchill's constant repetition of the word "victory" and his description of Nazism as a

"monstrous tyranny."

3. On the lines below, briefly state how propaganda is used or described in the two statements.

Answers will vary but should refer to efforts on both sides to rally public opinion behind the war effort.

 # Standardized Test Skills Practice

DIRECTIONS: Based on the readings and the poster, answer the following questions.

1 The aim of the U.S. war poster on the previous page is to _____

   A promote unity among the Allies.

   B encourage people to buy war bonds.

   C rally volunteers to join the armed forces.

   *D urge workers to increase industrial output and win the war.

2 In his speech, Winston Churchill aims to boost British support for the war effort by _____

   F appealing to past British military victories and the glories of empire.

   *G describing the war as a struggle against evil on which British survival depends.

   H disguising the horror and struggle of war with stirring language.

   J appealing to the pro-German sympathies of British public opinion.

Standardized Test Skills Practice

ACTIVITY 27
Interpreting and Writing Editorials

Social Studies Objective: The student will recognize points of view, propaganda, and/or statements of fact and nonfact in a variety of written texts.
Social Studies Objective: The student will generate a written composition that develops/supports/elaborates the central idea stated in a given topic.

An article written for publication that expresses the writer's opinion on an issue is known as an **editorial.** In some editorials the writer makes a strong case for his or her opinion, but in other editorials the writer may contrast several viewpoints as background for presenting his or her own position on the issue. As with a political cartoon, the purpose of an editorial is to influence public opinion and to generate discussion.

★ Learning to Interpret and Write an Editorial

Use the following guidelines to help you write editorials.

- Focus on the subject and purpose.
- Familarize yourself with the pros and cons of the subject as well as the facts that support both sides.

- Develop your own viewpoint with information that will add authority and interest to your writing.
- Present information in order of importance. Start with the most important points.

★ Practicing the Skill

DIRECTIONS: Read the selection below and complete the activity that follows.

The North Atlantic Treaty Organization (NATO)

NATO is a political and military alliance formed in 1949 among Western European states, Canada, and the United States to prevent Soviet expansion into Western Europe. It was designed to establish a balance to Soviet military power, including its nuclear threat. The North Atlantic Treaty establishing NATO stated that an armed attack against one or more of the NATO members would be considered as an attack on all members.

Twelve nations signed the North Atlantic Treaty in 1949. They were Belgium, Great Britain, Canada, Denmark, France, Iceland, Italy, Luxembourg, the Netherlands, Norway,

Portugal, and the United States. Greece and Turkey signed the treaty in 1951, West Germany in 1954, and Spain in 1982. West Germany had been created in 1949, when the nation of Germany was divided into eastern and western parts. In 1990, following the collapse of the communist Warsaw Pact, Germany was reunited and replaced West Germany as a NATO member.

After the Warsaw Pact's collapse, NATO made its forces available for peacekeeping missions to non-NATO European countries, especially those in the war-torn Balkan Peninsula. It also began to cooperate with former Warsaw Pact members. By the late 1990s, several of these formerly Communist countries were seeking membership in the NATO alliance.

DIRECTIONS: Editorials appeal to both reason and emotion in persuading people to accept a given viewpoint. In early 1998, a debate began on what the response of the United States should be to the admission of former Communist nations to the NATO alliance. Study the following editorial from the *Dallas Morning News,* March 2, 1998, and answer the questions that follow.

The Senate should ratify NATO membership for Poland, Hungary, and the Czech Republic.

If it declines, those nations would inhabit a "gray zone" of insecurity between NATO and Russia, increasing the risk of instability and the likelihood that the United States would be drawn into another European war.

The concerns about Russia are legitimate. But Russia is getting used to having lost its vassal states. It is beginning to understand that NATO membership for Poland, Hungary, and the Czech Republic will make it more not less secure. Its people are more concerned about economic opportunity and strengthening democracy than about NATO. Barring some unlikely authoritarian backlash, its parliament will ratify the nuclear arms treaty.

One benefit would be psychological. At last, the artificial line dividing West and East would be erased. As NATO members, Poland, Hungary, and the Czech Republic would retake their place in the community of Euro-Atlantic democracies, from which they were forcibly separated after World War II.

NATO is emerging as something radically new. Don't think of it anymore as a lot of tanks, troops, and airplanes congregated along a long front. Think of it as projecting stability and managing crises in a broader strategic sense. Bosnia is just one example of the kind of "out of area" mission that NATO might undertake in the future.

Cold War or no Cold War, there is value in collective defense. Like it or not, the United States needs allies who share its values. The Senate should ratify expansion, and by more than the required two-thirds majority.

1. What is the subject and purpose of the editorial?

U.S. Senate should support admission of three former Communist nations to NATO.

2. Review the editorial regarding NATO expansion. On a separate sheet of paper, write an editorial expressing your own point of view on the issue. Be specific. Which position do you support and why? Give reasons why you *do not* support the opposing position.

Answers will vary; students should clearly support one position and reject another.

 # Standardized Test Skills Practice

DIRECTIONS: Answer the following questions.

1 Which of the following statements would an opponent of NATO admission make?

  *A It increases the danger of involving Americans in war.

  B NATO has been successful in solving crises in recent years.

  C Eastern Europe's new governments deserve security.

  D Russia will accept expansion.

2 According to the editor, what is a *major* argument for supporting the new NATO expansion?

  F Russia is upset about losing its allies.

  G The cost of expanding NATO is not significant.

  H Russia will reduce its nuclear arms even if the expansion takes place.

  *J NATO provides a collective defense against instability and crises.

Standardized Test Skills Practice

ACTIVITY 28
Perceiving Cause-and-Effect Relationships

Social Studies Objective: The student will perceive relationships and recognize outcomes in a variety of written texts.

Any condition or event that makes something happen is known as a **cause.** What happens as a result of a cause is an effect. Cause-and-effect relationships explain why things happen and how actions produce other actions. Cause-and-effect relationships can be simple or complex. Sometimes several different causes produce a single effect. On the other hand, one cause can produce several effects.

★ Learning to Perceive Cause and Effect

Use the following guidelines to help you perceive cause-and-effect relationships.

- Select an event.
- Compare the situation at the time of the event with conditions before it happened (*causes*) and after it happened (*effects*).
- Look for vocabulary clues to help decide whether one event caused another. Words or phrases such as *brought about, produced,*

resulted in, when, and *therefore* indicate cause-and-effect relationships.
- Describe the causes and effects of the event.
- Look for other relationships between the events. Check for other, more complex, connections beyond the immediate cause and effect.

★ Practicing the Skill

DIRECTIONS: Read the selection below and complete the activity that follows.

Russia's Dramatic Past

Czars' coat of arms

Over the centuries Russia grew as its czars (emperors) conquered other lands. Czars such as Peter I and Catherine II pushed the empire's borders westward and southward. They also tried to make Russia more like Europe. A new capital—St. Petersburg—was built in the early 1700s to look like a European city.

The actions of the czars, however, had little effect on ordinary citizens. Most Russians were serfs, or laborers who were bound to the land. In 1861 Czar Alexander II freed the serfs.

Russia, however, did not progress politically. The czars clung to their power and rejected democracy. Revolution brewed. In 1917 the political leaders and workers forced Czar Nicholas II to give up the throne. At the end of the year, a group of Communists led by Vladimir Ilyich Lenin came to power. They set up a Communist government and soon moved its capital to Moscow. In 1922 the Communists formed the Union of Soviet Socialist Republics, or the Soviet Union.

During the late 1920s, Joseph Stalin became the ruler of the Soviet Union and set out to make it a great industrial power. To reach this goal, the government took control of all industry and farming. Stalin, a cruel dictator, put down any opposition to his rule. Millions of people were either killed or sent to prison labor camps.

After World War II the Soviet Union further expanded its territory and extended communism to Eastern Europe. From the late 1940s to the late 1980s, the Soviet Union and the United States waged a Cold War. They competed for world influence without actually waging war on each other.

In 1985 Mikhail Gorbachev came to power in the Soviet Union. In addition to economic changes, he supported a policy of *glasnost*, or openness. He wanted people to speak freely about the Soviet Union's problems. Gorbachev's efforts, however, failed to stop the collapse of the Soviet Union. Many of the non-Russian nations had long resented Russian rule and wanted independence. By late 1991, the Soviet Union had broken apart and Russia had a new leader, Boris Yeltsin. Economic and social problems continue as Russia seeks to move to a free market economy.

DIRECTIONS: When studying details about a long period of time like the history of Russia, a graphic organizer can help in understanding causes and effects. Fill in the graphic organizer below with information you just read. Fill in the missing causes or effects of various events in Russian history. To get you started, one cause-and-effect relationship has been given.

Cause	Effect
• Czars kept political power and rejected democracy.	• Russian Revolution of 1917
• Stalin wants to make the Soviet Union into an industrial power.	• *The government took control of industry and farming.*
• *Stalin put down opposition by force.*	• Millions were killed or put in camps
• The Soviet Union expanded territory after World War II.	• *Communism spread.*
• *Policy of* glasnost *supported.*	• People criticize government.
• Resentment of non-Russians and mounting economic problems	• *Russian Revolution of 1991*

Standardized Test Skills Practice

DIRECTIONS: After reading the selection on the previous page, answer the following questions.

1   What was the primary reason for the Russian Revolution of 1917?

   A   Czar Alexander II built the Trans-Siberian Railroad.

   B   Czar Alexander II freed the serfs and initiated reforms.

   *C   Czar Nicholas II clung to power and rejected reforms.

   D   Russia expanded its territory by conquering other lands.

2   The policy of *glasnost* refers to _____

   F   Czar Alexander II freeing the serfs.

   G   building a transcontinental railroad.

   H   expanding Russian territory.

   *J   democratic reforms under Mikhail Gorbachev.

Standardized Test Skills Practice

ACTIVITY 29
Developing a Process to Solve a Problem

Social Studies Objective: The student will organize ideas in a written composition on a given topic.

A logical sequence of steps directed toward the solution of a problem is known as a **process.** When you develop a process for problem solving, you first look closely at the problem and analyze the problem's causes and effects. Then you present the detailed steps involved in completing the process and reaching a solution.

★ Learning to Develop and Write about a Process

Use the following guidelines to help you develop and write about a process that is directed toward solving a problem.

- Identify the problem and its probable causes and effects.
- Study possible solutions and evaluate the *pros* and *cons* of each.
- Identify the steps of a process for solving the problem. Arrange the steps in chronological order. Explain one step at a time.

- Provide supporting information.
- Use transition words such as *first, next, then,* and *finally* to point the way as you write.
- Check to make sure your explanation is complete and accurate.
- Suggest or carry out a solution and evaluate its effects.

★ Practicing the Skill

DIRECTIONS: In recent years many people have become concerned about deforestation—the cutting down and clearing away of trees—in the world's rain forests. Study the information below on deforestation in South America's Amazon River basin. Then complete the activity that follows.

Deforestation Activities
Activities that have contributed to the loss of 10 percent of the Amazon rain forest:
- construction of roads
- clearing land by slash-and-burn methods
- development of commercial cattle ranches
- use of trees for lumber and other products

Major Concerns
Opinions differ concerning the effects of deforestation; however, most experts agree that:
- deforestation will upset the heat balance, causing dangerous warming.
- it will upset the water cycle.
- it will cause the extinction of plants/animals.
- it will produce a less healthy secondary forest.

Name _____ Date _____ Class _____

DIRECTIONS: Developing a process to solve a problem involves comparing different types of information. Study the photo on the previous page, the map of the Amazon rain forest, and the list of Brazilian government policies shown below. After analyzing this data, answer the following questions that will help you develop a problem-solving process.

Brazilian Government Policies
- Squatters can get title by using land.
- Cattle ranching is heavily subsidized.
- Financial incentives are awarded for clearing forests.
- Dam projects have affected millions of acres.
- Government-directed colonization has brought new settlers into the Amazon region.
- Income from agriculture is exempt from income tax.

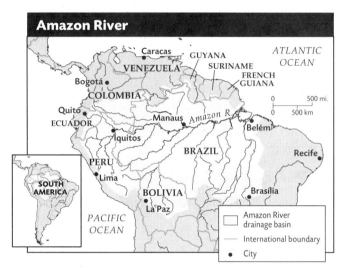

1. What problem is presented in the data? What are its probable causes and effects?

   Problem: deforestation in the Amazon River basin

   Causes: highway construction; clearing land by slash-and-burn
   farming; development of settlements and ranches; use of trees for lumber and
   other products

   Effects: upset heat balance and water cycle; produce a less healthy secondary forest; cause
   extinction of plants and animals

2. What steps would you propose to solve the problem? Briefly list below the steps of a process directed toward a solution. *Steps will vary according to the problem-solving process.*

   A. *Answer will vary.* **C.** *Answer will vary.*
   B. *Answer will vary.* **D.** *Answer will vary.*

   Solution: *Answer will vary but should be based on students' processes.*

Standardized Test Skills Practice

DIRECTIONS: On a separate sheet of paper, write two or three paragraphs explaining your process for solving the problems of the Amazon River basin. Assume that your audience is fellow students who are unfamiliar with both the topic and the process.

Answer will vary but should follow the guidelines for developing and writing about a process.

Standardized Test Skills Practice

ACTIVITY 30
Writing a News Story

Social Studies Objective: The student will organize ideas in a written composition on a given topic.

*T*he primary purpose of a **news story** is to provide the latest information about current affairs to the reader. In a news story, the first paragraph—the lead—captures attention and summarizes the main points of the story. Other details are related in decreasing order of importance. Most of the details in a news story are facts—statements, events, and observations—that can be proved or disproved. The goal of a news story is to answer six basic questions (the 5 *Ws* and one *H*)—*Who? What? Where? When? Why?* and *How?*

★ Learning to Write a News Story

Use the following guidelines to help you write a news story.

- Gather information that will add authority and interest to your writing.
- Write a strong lead. Grab the reader's attention and summarize your main points.
- Present the details in order of importance. Start with the most important points.

- Be fair. Cover all sides of the story, and keep your own opinions out of your article.
- Make sure your facts are accurate and that proper names are spelled correctly.

★ Practicing the Skill

DIRECTIONS: Read the following news story and complete the activity that follows.

Emotional Visit to Robben Island for Clinton and Mandela

March 27, 1998

CAPE TOWN, South Africa (PANA) – U.S. President Bill Clinton on Friday had an emotional visit to the Robben Island prison cell where South Africa President Nelson Mandela spend 18 years of his 27 year term in prison.

The two revered statesmen walked with arms around each other down the dark corridor leading to the B section where the two square metre cell is.

"This was home," Mandela said to the visibly moved Clinton. "You know, it was so big at the time, I don't know why it's small now."

They spent several minutes in the cell, with Clinton's wife Hillary and Mandela's companion Graca Machel. The two men peered out of the cell window into the high-walled courtyard that blocks any view of the Atlantic Sea.

The cell has been restored to how it was when he was jailed, sparsely furnished with a few blankets and a metal plate and cup.

The two leaders also drove past the lime quarry where Mandela and other political prisoners were forced to do hard labour. Mandela's early years at Robben Island were spent working in a limestone quarry which has seriously affected his eyesight.

Mandela was shipped to the wind-swept island in Cape Town's Table Bay in 1964, immediately after being sentenced to life imprisonment for plotting to overthrow the apartheid government.

The prison was closed down in 1996, and it is now a popular tourism attraction. On Saturday, the visiting president is scheduled to fly to Johannesburg.

Clinton is winding up his three-day visit of South Africa Sunday. From South Africa, he [is] scheduled to proceed to Botswana for a meeting with outgoing President Ketumile Masire, who is retiring.

The U.S. President is on an 11-day African tour that has so far led him to Ghana, Uganda, Rwanda before coming here. The U.S. President is expected to arrive in Senegal next Tuesday.

(Copyright© 1998 Panafrican News Agency. Distributed via **Africa News Online (www.africanews.org)**

DIRECTIONS: Most of the details in a news story are facts. Use information from the preceding news story to answer the six basic questions of news writing in the chart below.

5 *Ws* and *H*

Who did it? Who caused the action? Who else is affected?

President Clinton and South African President Nelson Mandela; the American and

South African people

What happened? What was the action? What were the reactions?

Clinton's visit to South Africa

When did it take place? When will related actions occur?

March 27, 1998

Where did it happen? What was the scene like?

Robben Island, a former prison colony in the waters off Cape Town

Why did it happen? Why was it significant?

to show Clinton the site of Mandela's imprisonment during the dark years of

apartheid in South Africa

How did it happen? How does it work? How will it affect people?

scheduled event demonstrating the positive changes in South Africa during the 1990s

 Standardized Test Skills Practice

DIRECTIONS: Use the guidelines to write a news story of about two to three paragraphs. Imagine that you are a reporter who was present on the historic day when the Republic of South Africa held its first election open to all races. Here are the facts for writing the news story:

- The election was held from April 26th to April 29th, 1994.
- About 22.7 million eligible voters participated in the four days of polling.
- Voters began standing in line at some polling stations at 4:00 A.M. on the first day of voting, with many waiting as long as 12 hours to cast their first ballots ever.
- The African National Congress (ANC) won a landslide victory, marking the end of a long struggle by South African blacks to achieve freedom from white-minority rule.
- ANC President Mandela proclaimed that black South Africans, who did not have the vote under apartheid, were "free at last."

News stories will vary but should make use of the facts provided.

Name ______________________ Date ______________ Class __________

Standardized Test Skills Practice

Activity 31
Using a Bar Graph to Interpret Data

Social Studies Objective: The student will express or solve problems using mathematical representation.
Social Studies Objective: The student will evaluate the reasonableness of a solution to a problem situation.

You can use a **bar graph** to compare different items or changes in the same item over time. The horizontal and vertical axes of a bar graph provide the structure for the data. When these axes represent numbers, each amount of space along an axis should represent the same unit or number.

★ Learning to Make a Bar Graph

DIRECTIONS: *Use the following guidelines when making bar graphs.*

- Collect statistical data for the bar graph.
- Create a grid with horizontal and vertical axes.
- Decide how each axis will be divided numerically. Label each unit.
- Give the graph a title and create bars by filling in data.

★ Practicing the Skill

DIRECTIONS: Read the following paragraph and study the table. Then complete the activity that follows.

Japan: An Economic Giant

Japan ended World War II with a ruined economy and a demoralized population. Out of defeat, however, it emerged as a vigorous industrial power. Although the Japanese economy slowed during the 1990s, it remains a major influence in global markets.

Since World War II, economic growth in Japan, as in other industrial nations, has raised the standard of living of its citizens. How do Japanese families spend their disposable (after-tax) income? The table below gives you average percentages of annual income spent on six necessities. It also shows the savings ratio. Three other industrial countries—the United States, Great Britain, and Germany—are included. If you were making a presentation to an audience, which would be more impressive—a table or a graph? Most people can make comparisons more easily with a visual such as a graph.

Household Expenditures of Disposable Income in Four Major Countries, 1997

		COUNTRY			
		Japan	United States	Great Britain	Germany
EXPENSES	Food	17.8%	10.7%	19.6%	21.1%
	Clothing	5.5%	5.8%	5.8%	6.9%
	Housing	26.7%	23.7%	25.5%	30.3%
	Medical Care	10.2%	17.7%	1.6%	6.2%
	Education	12.8%	10.2%	10.0%	11.1%
	Transportation	11.1%	13.1%	17.6%	16.2%
	Savings Ratio	12.8%	3.9%	5.7%	11.6%

Source: Government of Japan

Name _____ Date _____ Class _____

DIRECTIONS: Bar graphs may be drawn vertically or horizontally. Study the table as well as the guidelines for making a bar graph. In the horizontal bar graph below, add the data from the table. Each listed item will show statistics for four countries. Use colors to distinguish the countries; add a key and a title.

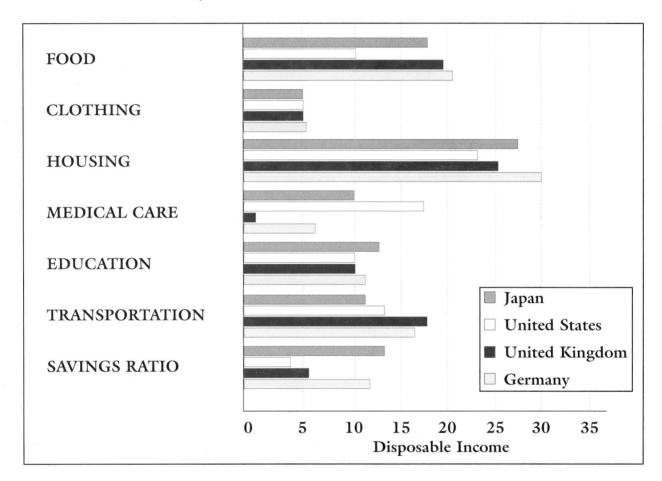

Standardized Test Skills Practice

DIRECTIONS: Answer the following questions based on the information in the bar graph.

1 What percentage of disposable income in Japan is spent on education?

A 17.8 %

B 11.1%

C 23.7%

*D 12.8%

2 Which country saves the smallest percentage of disposable income?

*F United States

G Japan

H Great Britain

J Germany

3 In what area do all four countries spend the largest amount of disposable income?

A Food

B Transportation

C Clothing

*D Housing

Standardized Test Skills Practice

ACTIVITY 32
Analyzing Statistics

Social Studies Objective: The student will express or solve problems using mathematical representation.
Social Studies Objective: The student will evaluate the reasonableness of a solution to a problem situation.

Sets of tabulated information, or **statistics,** may be gathered through surveys and other sources. When studying statistics consider the following:
- Two types of samples are a **biased sample,** one that does not represent the whole population, and an **unbiased sample,** called a representative sample.
- A **correlation** can be *positive* if there is a relationship between two sets of data or *negative* if no relationship exists.
- A **statistical significance** exists if there is a probability of less than 5 percent that the results are due to chance.

★ Learning to Analyze Statistics

Use the following guidelines to help you analyze statistical data.

- Determine if there is a correlation among the data.
- Draw conclusions about the importance of the correlating data.

★ Practicing the Skill

DIRECTIONS: Read the selection and study the table below. Complete the activity that follows.

The Organization of Petroleum Exporting Countries (OPEC)

Eleven countries belong to an oil cartel (alliance) called OPEC. Established in 1960, OPEC controls 40 percent of the world's oil production. With the exception of Venezuela, Nigeria, and Indonesia, all of OPEC's members are Middle Eastern or North African nations. The purpose of OPEC is to control the global supply of oil.

OPEC countries meet twice a year to set quotas for production. Recently, Venezuela refused to attend an OPEC meeting and declared that it intended to increase production above the quotas set by the members. Their energy minister announced, "The age of [OPEC production] quotas is finished." Since his announcement, oil prices have fallen to the lowest level in four years.

Economic Profile of Selected OPEC Countries				
	IRAN	IRAQ	KUWAIT	SAUDI ARABIA
Population in Millions	66.1	21.4	2.0	19.4
Per Capita GDP	5,300	2,000	16,100	10,200
Crude Oil Production (1,000 barrels)	3,675	600	2,060	8,083
Share of Oil in GDP	16%	50%	45%	30%
Automobile Registrations (Units per 1,000 persons)	25	34	296	82

Source: CIA Publications, OPEC Profile, 1997

Name _____ Date _____ Class _____

DIRECTIONS: In statistics, two or more sets of data may be related or unrelated. Study the graphs below and answer the questions that follow.

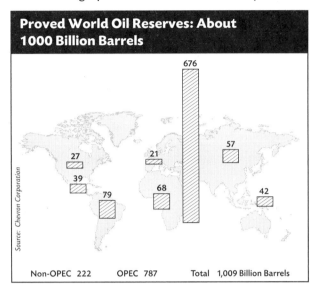

Proved World Oil Reserves: About 1000 Billion Barrels

676

27
39
79
21
68
57
42

Source: Chevron Corporation

Non-OPEC 222   OPEC 787   Total 1,009 Billion Barrels

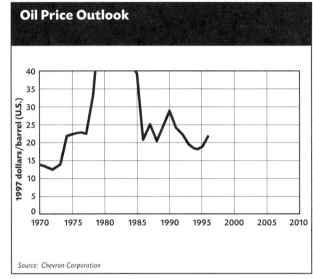

Oil Price Outlook

Source: Chevron Corporation

1. Which continent has the least oil reserves?
 A. Asia   ***C.** Europe
 B. North America   **D.** South America

2. What correlation might exist between OPEC oil reserves and oil prices in the future?
 ***A.** OPEC oil production will continue to have an important impact on oil prices.
 B. Oil prices will remain stable in the future regardless of OPEC production.
 C. Oil reserves are limited and oil prices will be climbing after the year 2005.
 D. There is a negative correlation between prices and production.

 # Standardized Test Skills Practice

DIRECTIONS: Study the table on the previous page and the graphs above. Answer the following questions.

1 What percent of Iraq's GDP comes from oil?

 A 25 percent

 B 15.6 percent

 ***C** 50 percent

 D 30 percent

2 Which country is most dependent on oil?

 F Iran

 ***G** Iraq

 H Kuwait

 J Saudi Arabia

3 Which country appears to have the highest standard of living?

 A Iran

 B Iraq

 ***C** Kuwait

 D Saudi Arabia

4 Which country could have the most impact on oil prices?

 F Iran

 G Iraq

 H Kuwait

 ***J** Saudi Arabia

64   *Glencoe World History*